P9-CLZ-901

# FUTURE

## *English for Results*

# 5

## TESTS and TEST PREP
with **Exam***View*® *Assessment Suite*

Wendy Pratt Long
Kathleen Smith

Series Consultants
Beatriz B. Díaz
Ronna Magy
Federico Salas-Isnardi

PEARSON
Longman

**Future 5 Tests and Test Prep**

Copyright © 2010 by Pearson Education, Inc.
All rights reserved.
The tests and test prep material in this publication are photocopiable. Pearson Education grants permission to classroom teachers to reproduce the tests for classroom use.

Permission is granted to reproduce the following for classroom use:
* Test taking strategies, pages viii–xviii
* Unit Tests pages 1–98
* Unit Test Answer sheet page 99

**Staff credits:** The people who made up the *Future 5 Tests and Test Prep* team, representing editorial, production, design, and manufacturing, are: Jennifer Adamec, Rhea Banker, Nancy Blodgett, Aerin Csigay, Nancy Flaggman, Irene Frankel, Katherine Keyes, Linda Moser, Barbara Sabella, Julie Schmidt, and Loretta Steeves
**Cover design:** Rhea Banker
**Cover photo:** Kathy Lamm/Getty Images
**Text composition:** TSI Graphics
**Text font:** Minion Regular
**Text design:** Barbara Sabella

**Photo Credits:** page 21 Photos.com/Jupiterimages; page 86 Shutterstock.

ISBN-13: 978-0-13-240925-4
ISBN-10: 0-13-240925-9

**PEARSON LONGMAN ON THE WEB**

**Pearsonlongman.com** offers online resources for teachers and students. Access our Companion Websites, our online catalog, and our local offices around the world.

Visit us at **www.pearsonlongman.com**.

Printed in the United States of America
5 16

# Contents

# Introduction

Welcome to *Future 5 Tests and Test Prep.* This package (containing a book, an audio CD, and a CD-ROM) provides all the assessment tools you need:

- The **Test Prep** section at the beginning of the book contains test-taking strategy worksheets and a sample unit test. These pages are photocopiable.
- The **Printed Unit Tests** in the book, also photocopiable, test students' mastery of the content presented in the Student Book units. The audio CD accompanies these tests.
- The **Exam***View®* *Assessment Suite* CD-ROM, found in the same envelope as the audio CD, offers a wealth of additional ways to assess students. Teachers can create their own unique tests. They can also print or customize already prepared unit tests in addition to midterm and final tests.

## Test Prep

### Test-Taking Strategy Worksheets

Many adult ESL students are unfamiliar with standardized tests. The Test Prep section contains reproducible worksheets that will prepare students for both the printed unit tests in this book and for any standardized tests they may have to take, such as the CASAS Life and Work Series. You will find the following worksheets on pages viii–x:

- How to Use an Answer Sheet
- Practice Questions for Standardized Tests
- Test-Taking Strategies

You can distribute the worksheets to your class over a period of time (for example, one page a week). Alternatively, you can wait until students are close to the time they will be tested or post-tested and then go over all the material in one session.

### Sample Unit Test

The Sample Unit Test gives students the opportunity to practice the kinds of questions they will answer in the Unit Tests. On pages xi–xviii you will find:

- Instructions for the Sample Unit Test
- Sample Unit Test
- Answer Key and Audio Script for the Sample Unit Test

To administer the Sample Unit Test:

- Go over the Instructions for the Sample Unit Test with your class.
- Make copies of the test and of the blank Answer Sheet on page 99. Distribute the copies to your students. Have them bubble in their test answers on the Answer Sheet.
- The audio for the sample listening questions can be found on the audio CD, Track 2. There are 10-second pauses after each conversation to allow students to respond to the questions.
- Check answers using the Answer Key and the Audio Script for the Sample Unit Test on page xviii.

The Sample Unit Test (with the exception of the grammar and writing sections) is similar in format and content to the CASAS Life and Work Reading and Listening Series tests, but not identical to them. The CASAS website (www.casas.org) offers additional information, such as practice test questions, that you may find useful.

## Printed Unit Tests

There are 10 printed Unit Tests in this test book. They are designed to assess how well students have mastered the material presented in each unit of the Student Book. Each test contains the following sections:

- Listening
- Life Skills
- Grammar
- Reading
- Writing

The Listening, Life Skills, and Reading sections of the tests emulate the look and feel of the CASAS Life and Work Reading and Listening Series tests. All the sections use a multiple-choice format, modeling the format students will encounter in standardized tests.

### Listening

The Listening section includes two or three sections. In all sections, students listen to test items and look at the answer choices on the test page.

In the first section, students hear a short conversation and have to answer a comprehension question about that conversation.

In the second section, students hear part of a conversation and have to choose the appropriate response to continue the conversation. This section is included only in Units 1–6.

In the last Listening section, students hear a conversation. They then hear three sentences about the conversation and have to choose which sentence is true.

The directions and the answer choices appear on the Listening test page. This is different from the CASAS test, where students are not given answer choices to look at. In other words, on the CASAS test, students bubble in their answers on the answer sheet, but they do not see the questions or answer choices in print. If your students need extra support, give them the Listening Test page when you distribute the test. But if you wish to emulate CASAS more closely, you should omit this page.

### Life Skills

In the Life Skills section, students read falsalia, such as a résumé or map. They then answer comprehension questions about it.

### Grammar

Students are asked to complete short conversations that contain examples of the grammar points presented in the unit.

### Reading

Students read short articles that reflect the grammar and themes covered in the unit and then answer comprehension questions about them.

### Writing

Students read paragraphs, letters, and other types of writing and answer questions that test their understanding of the writing skills presented in the unit.

### Answer Keys and Audio Scripts

You will find an Answer Key and an Audio Script for each printed Unit Test at the back of this book. The Answer Key is an answer sheet with the correct answers for the test bubbled in. It also provides diagnostic information about each test question. The Audio Script includes the conversations and comprehension questions. The direction lines and answer choices, which are also recorded, appear only on the test page.

### Administering and Scoring Printed Unit Tests

To administer a printed Unit Test:

- Find the test you want in this book and photocopy it.
- Decide whether or not you want students to look at the Listening page as they take the test (see the Listening section). Either include or omit the Listening page when you distribute the test.
- Make copies of the blank Answer Sheet on page 99 and distribute them to your students. Ask students to bubble in their test answers on the Answer Sheet.

- Start with the Listening section of the test. Locate the appropriate audio track on the audio CD. Note that each item of the Listening section has a separate track. We recommend that you play each track twice, pausing for 10 to 20 seconds between each play. This will approximate how listening is presented on standardized tests.
- Each 33-item test is designed to take 25 to 30 minutes to administer.

To score a printed Unit Test:

- Collect your students' bubbled-in Answer Sheets.
- Locate the Answer Key for the test at the back of this book. To create a scoring mask, photocopy the Answer Key and punch a hole in each bubbled-in answer. When you lay this scoring mask over a student's Answer Sheet, you can easily see if the student has bubbled in the correct answer. If the bubble is not filled in, then simply mark an *X* on the unmarked bubble with a colored pencil.
- Count the number of correctly bubbled-in answers on the student's Answer Sheet. Each correct answer is worth three points. To calculate a percentage score for your students, multiply the number of correct answers by three and add one point.

The Answer Key provides the objective that each item tests, along with the lesson and page number in the Student Book where the material was presented. If a student answers a particular item incorrectly, you will then know which competency the student has missed and/or in which lesson he or she may need further practice.

## **Exam***View*® *Assessment Suite*

The **Exam***View*® *Assessment Suite* can be used either to supplement the printed Unit Tests or in place of them. With **Exam***View*, you can create or customize your own tests for students. Alternatively, you can choose to simply print out Unit, Midterm, or Final tests that have already been prepared for you and administer them to your class.

For detailed information on how to install the **Exam***View* software and use it to create, customize, and print out tests, please refer to the *TO THE TEACHER* PDF located on the *Future 5* **Exam***View Assessment Suite* CD-ROM. The installation instructions in the back of the book will tell you how to find this document.

### **Exam***View* **Unit Tests**

The **Exam***View* unit tests have the same general structure as the printed Unit Tests in the book, with a series of multiple choice questions that test listening, life skills, grammar, reading, and writing skills. However, the **Exam***View* unit tests do not follow the CASAS testing format as closely as the printed Unit Tests do. Another difference is that there are two separate types of tests for each unit. The first is a Listening Test in PDF format. The Listening Tests are offered in PDF format to make them easier for teachers to administer. Students listen to longer conversations (similar to the listenings in the Student Book) and then answer comprehension questions about them.

The second type of test is an **Exam***View* Test, containing life skills, grammar, reading, and writing items.

### **Exam***View* **Midterm and Final Tests**

The **Exam***View* Midterm and Final Tests provide an objective, standardized way to assess all your students at the halfway point and at the end of the course. The tests have a total of 66 items each. The Midterm tests the content presented in Units 1–5 and the Final covers Units 6–10. As with the Unit Tests, the Listening Midterm and Final Tests are in PDF format, and life skills, grammar, reading, and writing items are in **Exam***View* question banks.

## Administering and Scoring Exam*View* Tests

To administer an **Exam***View* Test:

- You can administer **Exam***View* Tests via computer or simply print them out and distribute them to your students. (The Listening Tests, as noted above, can only be administered in print format.)
- Locate the appropriate PDFs and **Exam***View* tests on the CD-ROM. For example, if you wanted to administer the tests for Unit 1, you would print out the Listening test PDF and the **Exam***View* test for Unit 1. (Please refer to the *TO THE TEACHER* PDF for more information on how to select the PDFs or tests you need.)
- Distribute the tests to your students. (Note: the Answer Keys for the **Exam***View* tests print out automatically at the end of the test. Make sure you do not distribute the Answer Key to your students along with the test!)
- If you are printing out tests for your students, make copies of the blank Answer Sheet on page 99. Distribute two copies to each student. One copy is for the Listening Test, and the other copy is for the **Exam***View* Test.
- Start with the Listening Test. Play the appropriate audio tracks for the test. The audio is located on the same CD-ROM as the **Exam***View* Software. It can be played on any CD player or computer with CD-playing software. Have students listen and fill in the correct number of bubbles on the first Answer Sheet (usually, for eight test items). Then collect the Listening Answer Sheets.
- Next, administer the **Exam***View* test for the unit. Have students bubble in the second Answer Sheet. Collect the Answer Sheets when students are finished.
- Allow 25–30 minutes for students to complete the Listening Test and the **Exam***View* test for each unit. Allow 50–60 minutes for a midterm or final.

To score an **Exam***View* Test:

- Collect your students' bubbled-in Answer Sheets.
- Locate the Answer Keys for the test. The Answer Keys and Audio Script for each Listening test are in PDF format in the same folder as the listening test. The Answer Keys for the **Exam***View* tests will print out automatically at the end of each test, as noted above.
- Count the number of correctly bubbled-in answers on each student's set of Answer Sheets. Add the scores of the Listening Test and the **Exam***View* test together. Then score the **Exam***View* Unit Tests as you would a printed Unit Test. For the 66-item Midterm or Final test, multiply the number of correct answers by 3, add 2 free points, and divide the result by 2 to get a percentage score.

You can find detailed diagnostic information about each test item in the Answer Keys, including the following:

- Level of difficulty (DIF)
- Reference (REF): Student Book level and unit being tested
- Learning objective (OBJ): the learning objective of the item (as found in the *Scope & Sequence*/Student Book unit lesson)
- National standard (NAT): the CASAS competency being tested, if applicable
- Skill (SKL): the skill being tested (listening, life skills, grammar, reading, or writing)

As with the printed Unit Test Answer Keys, you can use this diagnostic information to determine the competencies and/or lessons in which your students need more practice.

## HOW TO USE AN ANSWER SHEET

For many tests, you use an Answer Sheet to mark, or bubble in, your answers. You must use a #2 pencil. You do not mark your answers on the test. A machine may score your answers. The machine reads and records the pencil marks on the Answer Sheet.

First, you need to fill in some personal information on the Answer Sheet.

Here is an example of the Answer Sheet in this book:

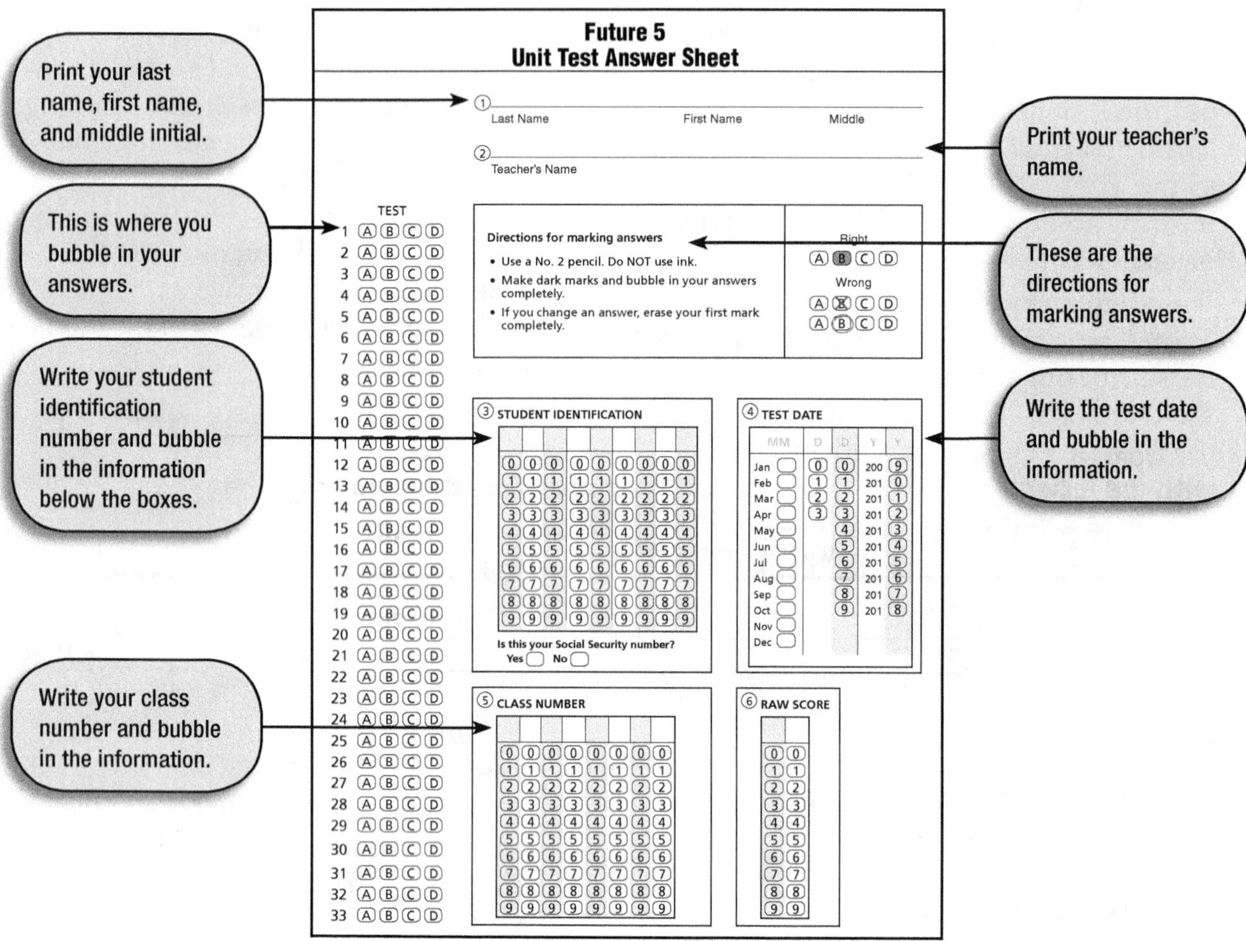


**Future 5**
**Unit Test Answer Sheet**

① Last Name First Name Middle

② Teacher's Name

TEST

1 A B C D
2 A B C D
3 A B C D
4 A B C D
5 A B C D
6 A B C D
7 A B C D
8 A B C D
9 A B C D
10 A B C D
11 A B C D
12 A B C D
13 A B C D
14 A B C D
15 A B C D
16 A B C D
17 A B C D
18 A B C D
19 A B C D
20 A B C D
21 A B C D
22 A B C D
23 A B C D
24 A B C D
25 A B C D
26 A B C D
27 A B C D
28 A B C D
29 A B C D
30 A B C D
31 A B C D
32 A B C D
33 A B C D

**Directions for marking answers**

- Use a No. 2 pencil. Do NOT use ink.
- Make dark marks and bubble in your answers completely.
- If you change an answer, erase your first mark completely.

Right: A B C D

Wrong: A B C D / A B C D

③ STUDENT IDENTIFICATION

Is this your Social Security number? Yes No

④ TEST DATE

MM D D Y Y

Jan, Feb, Mar, Apr, May, Jun, Jul, Aug, Sep, Oct, Nov, Dec

200 9, 201 0, 201 1, 201 2, 201 3, 201 4, 201 5, 201 6, 201 7, 201 8

⑤ CLASS NUMBER

⑥ RAW SCORE

## PRACTICE QUESTIONS FOR STANDARDIZED TESTS

Many standardized tests begin with a practice page. Here is an example of a practice page. Read through the questions below and make sure you understand how to answer them.

When you take a standardized test, find the practice page. It says Practice. Look for the practice answer box on the answer sheet. Use a pencil. Bubble in your answer. Ask the tester for help if you do not understand the directions. When the test begins, you are not allowed to talk. You cannot ask for or give help.

## READING TEST

### Practice

**PREVIOUS EMPLOYER**

| | | |
|---|---|---|
| EMPLOYER<br>Koll's | ADDRESS<br>2200 E. Elm Street Monterey Park, CA 91754 | |
| SUPERVISOR<br>Victor Santoro | PHONE #<br>(520) 555-9875 | May we contact? [X] YES [ ] NO |
| STARTING POSITION<br>Clerk | ENDING POSITION<br>Clerk | |
| DATES WORKED<br>03/15/08 – 04/28/10 | JOB DUTIES<br>worked cash register, customer service | |
| SALARY/WAGE<br>$6.75/hr | REASON FOR LEAVING<br>wanted more hours | |

APPLICANT SIGNATURE: Li Chiu DATE: October 14, 2010

1. Why did Li Chiu leave his job with Koll's?
   A. He wanted a better salary.
   B. He wanted to work more hours.
   C. He was moving to a new address.
   D. He wanted to work at the cash register.

PRACTICE

| | | | | |
|---|---|---|---|---|
| 1 | (A) | (B) filled | (C) | (D) |
| 2 | (A) | (B) | (C) | (D) |

## TEST-TAKING STRATEGIES

### Preparing to Take a Test

- Get a lot of sleep the night before the test.
- Eat a meal or snack before the test.
- Bring two sharpened #2 pencils.
- Bring a pencil eraser.
- Bring a ruler or a blank piece of paper.
- Arrive early to the testing room.
- Make sure you can easily see and hear the tester.
- Turn off your cell phone.
- Try to relax and do your best! Good luck!

### Taking a Test

- As soon as you start a test section, look through the section to see how many questions there are.
- Don't spend too much time on any one question. If you don't know the answer, guess and then move on to the next item. You can circle the item number and come back to it at the end if you have time.
- For a listening section: Look at the answer choices for the question. Then listen to the directions and the question. Remember that for some questions, both questions and answer choices may be on the CD. You will hear the questions and the answer choices.
- For all other sections: Read the material. Read the question carefully. Read all the answer choices.
- Think: Which is the best answer? Look at the answer choices again. Eliminate answers you know are not correct.
- Choose the best answer.
- Make sure you mark your answer on the correct line on the answer sheet. Use a ruler to help you, or use a blank piece of paper to cover the lines below the line you are working on.
- Check each time that you bubble in the circle on the correct line for the question you are answering.
- Do not change the first answer you mark unless you are sure that it is wrong.
- Erase completely any answers you have changed. Fill in only ONE answer on each line. Erase all extra marks on your answer sheet.
- When you finish, if there is time, always recheck your answers.
- If you cannot answer many questions, it is OK. Raise your hand. Tell the tester. You may be excused from taking the rest of the test.

## INSTRUCTIONS FOR THE SAMPLE UNIT TEST

This sample test is like the Unit Tests in this book. It has Listening, Life Skills, Grammar, Reading, and Writing questions. Follow the directions carefully.

### Listening Section

All the questions in the Listening section have three answer choices. Here are examples of the three types of listening questions:

**Example 1:** You listen to a conversation and choose the correct answer to a question about it. You will hear the question both before and after the conversation.
**You will hear:** What does the woman want to do?

**F:** *I need to make an appointment with Dr. Chang.*
**M:** *OK. When would you like to come in?*
**F:** *Can I come in next Tuesday morning?*

What does the woman want to do?

A. She wants to see the doctor on Tuesday.
B. She wants a job at a doctor's office.
C. She wants to cancel an appointment.

**The correct answer is A.**

**Example 2:** You listen to the first part of a conversation and choose what the person will say next.
**You will hear:** **F:** *Want to go to the movies tonight?*
**M:** *Sorry. I have to work late tonight.*

A. OK. Let's meet at 6:00.
B. That's a really good movie.
C. Too bad. How about tomorrow night?

**The correct answer is C.**

**Example 3:** You listen to a conversation and choose which sentence about it is true.
**You will hear:** **F:** *When did you start working at Al's Electronics?*
**M:** *Three years ago. I worked one year as a stock clerk and then I became a sales assistant.*

Which sentence is true?

A. The man worked in an electronics store for one year.
B. The man was a stock clerk before he was a sales assistant.
C. The man is working as a stock clerk now.

**The correct answer is B.**

### Life Skills Section

The questions in the Life Skills sections have four answer choices. You read a short piece of information, such as a form, label, or map. You then answer questions about the information.

### Grammar Section

The questions in the Grammar section have three answer choices. You read a short conversation and choose the correct answer to complete the conversation.

### Reading Section

The questions in the Reading section have four answer choices. You read a short passage and then answer questions about the passage.

### Writing Section

The questions in the Writing section have four answer choices. You read a paragraph, letter, or other type of writing and then answer questions about it.

## SAMPLE UNIT TEST

### LISTENING I

***(Track 2)* You will hear a question. Then you will hear a conversation. After that, you will hear the question again and three choices. What is the correct answer: A, B, or C?**

**1.** A. The child probably broke his leg.
B. The child probably bruised his leg.
C. The child probably broke his ankle.

### LISTENING II

**You will hear the first part of a conversation. To finish the conversation, listen and choose the correct answer: A, B, or C.**

**2.** A. My kids are older now, so it's not a problem.
B. My family is happy about it.
C. I'm working at night.

### LISTENING III

**You will hear a conversation. Then you will hear three sentences. Which sentence is true: A, B, or C?**

**3.** A. The man wants to be a construction worker.
B. The man wants to go to college.
C. The man wants to own a large company.

## LIFE SKILLS

### Read. What is the correct answer: A, B, C, or D?

| Current Charges | Amount |
|---|---|
| Customer charge<br>30 Days | 4.93 |
| Gas and Electricity Charges | 140.07 |
| Taxes and Fees | 4.78 |
| Total gas charges (Including taxes and fees) | 149.78 |
| **Total Amount Now Due** | **149.78** |

Current Amount Past Due if not paid by Nov 30, 2010.
A late charge of $5.00 may apply.

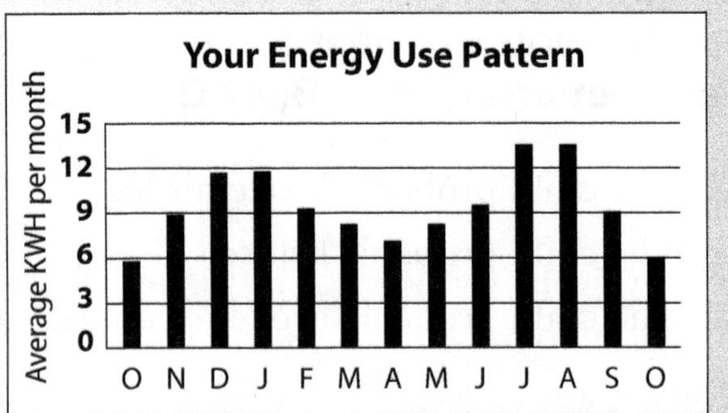


*ENERGY SAVING TIP To save on your heating bill, set the thermostat lower. If you lower the thermostat slowly, over a few weeks, you will get used to the lower temperature.*

****Special Discount***You may be eligible for California Alternate Rates for Energy (CARE) program. For more information and to request an application, please call 1-800-772-5050.*

**4.** How much does the customer owe the electric company?

A. $4.93

B. $140.07

C. $4.78

D. $149.78

**5.** In which month did the customer use the most electricity?

A. April

B. August

C. October

D. December

## GRAMMAR

### Complete each conversation. What is the correct answer: A, B, or C?

6. **A:** I'm planning to go to school this fall.
   **B:** What courses _______ to take?

   A. will you
   B. you're going
   C. are you going

7. **A:** Have you ever _______ a computer class?
   **B:** Yes. I took a class at night last year.

   A. taken
   B. taking
   C. take

## READING

### Read. What is the correct answer: A, B, C, or D?

Min-Ji Lee came to the United States with almost no money and with very little English. Today she is the owner of a popular toy store, Min-Ji's Magic House. Min-Ji achieved her goal through hard work and creative thinking. Min-Ji's father was a carpenter in Korea, and he had taught her how to work with wood. So, when Min-Ji first arrived in the United States, she got a job at a furniture factory. She worked long hours to save money, and she took English classes on the weekends. Min-Ji enjoyed her job, but she wanted something more. One day, she realized that the factory was throwing out a lot of extra, small pieces of wood. Min-Ji had an idea. She got permission from her manager to take some of the wood home. At home, she used the wood to create a child's toy. She gave the toy to a friend's child. Her friend liked the toy and encouraged Min-Ji to make more. Soon, Min-Ji realized she had enough money to quit her job and pursue her dream of owning her own business. Five years ago, she opened her first store. Min-Ji's Magic House is a great success. Min-Ji plans to open a second store soon. She says, "My father taught me carpentry, but he also taught me something else. He taught me to have a dream and to follow it."

**8.** What is the main idea of the story?

A. Min-Ji learned carpentry from her father in Korea.

B. Min-Ji achieved her dream through hard work and creativity.

C. Min-Ji took English classes on the weekends.

D. Min-Ji had to save up a lot of money to start her business.

**9.** What was Min-Ji's first job in the United States?

A. She was an assistant in a toy store.

B. She was a carpenter in her father's store.

C. She was a toy designer working at home.

D. She was a furniture-maker in a factory.

**10.** Based on the information in the story, what inference can you make?

A. Min-Ji works harder now than she did in the past.

B. Min-Ji enjoys making toys more than making furniture.

C. Min-Ji did not have a good relationship with her father.

D. Min-Ji's friend gave her money to help her start her business.

## WRITING

Manuel Lopez
1520 N. Calle Verde
Tucson, AZ 85745

August 25, 2010

Barbara Weiss, Manager
Arnold's Steak House
2880 E. Broadway
Tucson, AZ 85701

Dear Ms. Weiss:

Thank you for the interview on Monday for the chef position at Arnold's Steak House. I enjoyed meeting you and learning more about the restaurant.

As I mentioned during the interview, I have experience managing a kitchen in a fast-paced restaurant. At my previous job, I worked long hours and was usually not paid overtime.

__________ (12.). Please call me at (520) 555-8958 if you have any more questions about my qualifications. I look forward to speaking with you soon.

Sincerely,

*Manuel Lopez*

Manuel Lopez

**11.** Which sentence should Manuel *not* include in the letter?

A. I enjoyed meeting you and learning more about the restaurant.
B. I have experience managing a kitchen in a fast-paced restaurant.
C. At my previous job, I worked long hours and was usually not paid overtime.
D. Please call me at (520) 555-8958 if you have any questions about my qualifications.

**12.** Which sentence should Manuel use to begin the last paragraph of the letter?

A. I think I would be a good addition to your staff.
B. I would like to start working on September 10.
C. I plan to take more culinary classes in the fall.
D. Please tell me if I will get the job.

## ANSWER KEY AND AUDIO SCRIPT FOR THE SAMPLE UNIT TEST

### Answer Key

| | |
|---|---|
| 1. B | 7. A |
| 2. A | 8. B |
| 3. B | 9. D |
| 4. D | 10. B |
| 5. B | 11. C |
| 6. C | 12. A |

### Audio Script *(Track 2)*

# LISTENING I

**1.** What does the woman think happened?

**F:** OK, sir, the ambulance will be there soon. So, your son fell out of a tree? Can you tell me more about his possible injuries?

**M:** Well, he's holding his leg and he's in a lot of pain. He's crying.

**F:** OK. Try to keep him calm, and keep his leg still. Is he bleeding?

**M:** No. I don't think so.

**F:** Well, maybe he just bruised his leg or sprained his ankle.

What does the woman think happened?

# LISTENING II

**2.** **M:** Hi, Maggie. It's nice to see you! What have you been doing lately?

**F:** I'm going to school now. I'm taking nursing classes at Westbrook Community College.

**M:** That's great. But how do you manage with your family?

# LISTENING III

3. **M:** I don't want to be a construction worker my whole life. I want to do something different.

**F:** Really? What do you think you want to do?

**M:** I'd like to get a degree in business and work for a large company.

Which sentence is true?

NAME ______________________

# Unit 1 Test

## LISTENING I

***(Tracks 3–6)*** **You will hear a question. Then you will hear a conversation. After that, you will hear the question again and three choices. What is the correct answer: A, B, or C?**

**1.** A. He's cooperative.
B. He's honest.
C. He's optimistic.

**2.** A. how to set a goal
B. how to choose a date for your outcome
C. how to overcome an obstacle

**3.** A. taking tests
B. communicating
C. solving problems

**4.** A. work as a restaurant manager
B. take culinary classes
C. start his own business

## LISTENING II

***(Tracks 7–8)*** **You will hear the first part of a conversation. To finish the conversation, listen and choose the correct answer: A, B, or C.**

**5.** A. Right now I'm going to school to be a nurse's assistant.
B. I want to get some information about starting a business.
C. In ten years, I want to be the manager of a hotel.

**6.** A. Yes, I'm intuitive.
B. Yes, I'm extroverted.
C. Yes, I have good interpersonal skills.

## LISTENING III

***(Tracks 9–10)*** **You will hear a conversation. Then you will hear three sentences. Which sentence is true: A, B, or C?**

**7.** A. The woman has gone on some job interviews.
B. The woman has gotten some informational interviews.
C. The man is helping the woman look for a job.

**8.** A. The man can't go to class anymore because of his work schedule.
B. The man isn't working now because he's taking classes.
C. The man dropped out of class because he had transportation problems.

NAME ____________________

## LIFE SKILLS

**Read the next page and answer these questions. What is the correct answer: A, B, C, or D?**

**9.** Which sentence is true about the person who completed the interests survey?
A. The person prefers working alone.
B. The person can follow instructions well.
C. The person doesn't like to do paperwork.
D. The person prefers a job that includes physical activity.

**10.** What does the person who completed the interests survey enjoy?
A. giving instructions to other people
B. making and creating things
C. working without instructions from another person
D. working with people

**11.** Which questions in the interests survey are related to interpersonal skills?
A. questions 1, 3, 4, and 14
B. questions 10, 12, 13, and 16
C. questions 6, 7, 9, and 11
D. questions 2, 5, 8, and 15

**12.** Which of the following types of skills are probably most important for working as a dental assistant?
A. math skills
B. problem-solving skills
C. communication skills
D. lifelong learning skills

**13.** What is one way that the job of dental assistant is a good match for the person who took the interests survey?
A. The person likes to use tools, and the job includes using tools.
B. The person likes to have supervision, and the job requires working under supervision.
C. The person has worked as a dental assistant, and the job requires experience.
D. The person likes to learn, and the job requires going to school for a long time.

| Interests Survey | Yes | No |
|---|---|---|
| 1. I like working with my hands. | | ✓ |
| 2. I enjoy helping others. | ✓ | |
| 3. I enjoy designing and producing things. | | ✓ |
| 4. I like to work with tools and machines. | | ✓ |
| 5. I like to be around people all day. | ✓ | |
| 6. I don't mind doing paperwork. | ✓ | |
| 7. I enjoy solving puzzles. | | ✓ |
| 8. I don't mind hearing other people's opinions and ideas. | ✓ | |
| 9. I'm good at following written instructions. | ✓ | |
| 10. I want to work in a quiet environment. | | ✓ |
| 11. I'm good at math. | ✓ | |
| 12. I want physical activity to be part of my job. | | ✓ |
| 13. I want to work without supervision. | | ✓ |
| 14. I enjoy creating things. | | ✓ |
| 15. I enjoy working as part of a group. | ✓ | |
| 16. I prefer working outside to working inside. | | ✓ |

### Dental Assistant

**Job description:** Assist dentists with patient care and office duties. Prepare equipment and materials for dental procedures. Provide assistance during dental procedures. Instruct patients on general oral care. Complete and organize forms and records. Maintain schedules and appointment book.

**Requirements:** Dental Assisting National Board certification or six months' experience. Must be able to work closely with and under the supervision of the employing dentist.

## GRAMMAR

### Complete each conversation. What is the correct answer: A, B, or C?

**14. A:** How would you feel about a job that requires working outdoors?
**B:** I really like _______ outside, so that would be good for me.

A. to be
B. being
C. Both A and B are correct.

**15. A:** Does Trisha mind _______ independently?
**B:** No, she works well by herself.

A. working
B. to work
C. Both A and B are correct.

**16. A:** Congratulations on your new job!
**B:** Thanks. I didn't plan _______ working so soon after school, but this job is a great opportunity.

A. to start
B. starting
C. Both A and B are correct.

**17. A:** Do you work well with others?
**B:** Yes, I work very well as part of a team. But I hate _______ other workers.

A. supervising
B. to supervise
C. Both A and B are correct.

**18. A:** What are you doing these days?
**B:** Well, I'm thinking about _______ back to school. I think I want to get an associate's degree in graphic design.

A. to go
B. going
C. Both A and B are correct.

**19. A:** Thank you for _______ the time to talk to me. I appreciate your help.
**B:** You're welcome. I'm glad I was able to help you.

A. to take
B. taking
C. Both A and B are correct.

**20. A:** What should I do before I go on an informational interview?
**B:** You should prepare for the interview by _______ a list of questions you want to ask.

A. making
B. to make
C. Both A and B are correct.

NAME____________________

# READING I

**Read the next page and answer these questions. What is the correct answer: A, B, C, or D?**

**21.** What is the main idea of this article?

A. Choosing a career is a big decision.

B. There are different ways to learn about specific careers.

C. It's important to learn about yourself and possible jobs before choosing a career.

D. You should do self-assessment before you investigate specific jobs.

**22.** According to the article, what should you do first?

A. match your interests and abilities to specific jobs

B. go to the U.S. Department of Labor's website

C. identify your interests and abilities

D. learn about specific careers

**23.** What is the purpose of self-assessment?

A. to learn more about certain jobs

B. to provide information to employers

C. to find tools for learning

D. to get information about yourself

**24.** What kinds of information can you get from the *Occupational Outlook Handbook*?

A. facts about the U.S. Department of Labor

B. predictions about the future of certain jobs

C. sample questions to ask at an informational interview

D. job openings in your area

**25.** Which of the following should usually *not* be part of a job interview?

A. questions about a typical workday

B. questions about common job duties

C. questions about working conditions

D. questions about salary

# CHOOSING A CAREER

Whether you're starting your first career or making a career change, choosing a career is a big decision. The first step in planning your career should involve self-assessment, or identifying some things about yourself, such as what you enjoy and what you're good at. Interest surveys and aptitude tests can help you learn about your interests, personality, skills, and abilities. You can find these tools at career centers and online. Self-assessment is important because it can help you make a decision about a career that's good for you. Once you complete your self-assessment, you can match your interests, personality, skills, and abilities to specific jobs.

The next step is to learn more about the jobs that match your interests and abilities. Online research can be a good way to get information. One very useful website is www.bls.gov. This is the website for the U.S. Department of Labor's *Occupational Outlook Handbook*. On that website you can investigate specific jobs to find out about what workers do, working conditions, projected job demand in the future, salaries, and training and education needed.

Another good way to learn about specific careers is to go on informational interviews. This means talking with someone who has a job you're interested in or a person who supervises workers with that job. The purpose of an informational interview is not to try to get a job, but to *learn* about a job. An informational interview can be less stressful than a typical job interview because you control the questions. You can ask questions about a typical workday, common job duties, and working conditions. In an informational interview, it's OK to ask some questions that you wouldn't usually ask in a job interview. For example, you can inquire about salary and benefits.

Choosing a career takes time and effort. But in the end it's worth it to choose carefully. It's a good idea to get as much information as you can to make an informed decision about a career that's good for *you*.

# READING II

**Read the next page and answer these questions. What is the correct answer: A, B, C, or D?**

**26.** What is the main idea of the essay?

A. It's difficult for many adults to go to English class every day.

B. The writer had a problem, and she worked to find a solution.

C. It's often hard for parents to go to English class.

D. If people work together, they can find solutions to most problems.

**27.** What was the writer's child-care solution at the beginning of the term?

A. Her sister took care of her son.

B. A classmate took care of her son.

C. Her neighbor took care of her son.

D. She and her neighbor took turns watching her son and her neighbor's kids.

**28.** What did the writer need in order to go back to class?

A. help from her neighbor

B. child care every day

C. an appointment with the school counselor

D. time to find someone to take care of her son

**29.** What was the final solution to the problem?

A. Students take turns missing class to watch all the children.

B. All students with children have class from 8:00 to 9:30.

C. Students watch one another's children.

D. A counselor watches students' children.

**30.** How does the writer probably feel now?

A. She's probably very excited that she finally learned English.

B. She's probably very glad to help her neighbor with her child-care problem.

C. She's probably very happy that her teacher solved the problem.

D. She's probably very proud that she figured out a solution to the problem.

## Search for a Solution By Ina Chomsky

I was very happy when I signed up to take an English class at the Adult Learning Center. I had wanted to take classes for a while, and I was proud and excited that I was finally going to improve my English. When I started the term, my sister took care of my son each morning while I was in class. But a month later, she got a job, and she had to work in the mornings. There wasn't anyone else who could watch my son while I was in class, so I had to drop out.

I really wanted to go back to class, but I couldn't figure out a solution to my child-care problem. One of my neighbors said that she could watch my son sometimes if I would do the same for her. It was a nice idea, but it wasn't good enough. I needed someone to take care of my son every day while I was in class. But then I started to think: if I was having problems finding child-care, other students probably were, too. Maybe there was a way we could help *one another* out. I talked with a counselor at our school, and together we came up with a plan.

We put signs up around the school that explained the new student-supported child-care program. Students who needed child-care while they were in class could sign up in the counselor's office. They wrote down which days and times they needed child-care. Then, they indicated a time when they could help take care of someone else's children. The counselor made up a schedule for students to take turns watching other students' children while they were in class.

Now I have class from 8 to 9:30 each morning. Students in another class watch my son and my classmates' children during that time. And from 9:30 to 11:00 I watch the children of other students. It's great—I get to study, and I have a way to help other students out.

NAME ____________________

## WRITING

### Read. What is the correct answer: A, B, C, or D?

**My Interests, Skills, and Goals**

__________ (31.). Even as a child, I loved helping my mother and grandmother in the kitchen. Today I love to try new recipes, and I also enjoy cooking without recipes sometimes. I use whatever ingredients I have, and I create something new.

I have a wide variety of skills. __________ (32.). I love word puzzles and number puzzles. I think my interpersonal skills are strong, too. I'm friendly and patient, and I'm a good listener. My friends often come to me for help, and I often help my friends with their problems.

I want to work at something that combines my interests and skills. My career goal is to work as a nutritionist at a school. __________ (33.). I'd like to show children that healthy eating can be delicious and fun. Right now I'm taking ESL classes at the community college. Next year I'll finish my ESL classes. Then I want to enroll as a credit student and study nutrition.

**31.** Which is the best topic sentence for the first paragraph?

A. When I was young, I wanted to be a chef.

B. Although I love food, I'm not a very good cook.

C. Cooking has always been one of my main interests.

D. Now I enjoy cooking more than I did when I was young.

**32.** Which sentence best supports the topic sentence of the second paragraph?

A. I'm good at math and problem solving.

B. I enjoy problem solving, but I work best in a quiet environment.

C. I would like to work with people and help them solve their problems.

D. I have a lot of experience working with people.

**33.** Which sentence best completes the third paragraph by giving details about the writer's goal?

A. I want to improve my eating habits so I can be healthier.

B. I think this will be a good job for me because I like food and cooking.

C. I'm interested in taking classes to learn about health, nutrition, and cooking.

D. I want to create nutrition programs for children and educate them about healthy eating.

NAME____________________

# Unit 2 Test

## LISTENING I

***(Tracks 11–13)* You will hear a question. Then you will hear a conversation. After that, you will hear the question again and three choices. What is the correct answer: A, B, or C?**

**1.** A. The woman should practice answers to interview questions.
B. The woman should wear a dress.
C. The woman should look neat and clean.

**2.** A. The man shouldn't take anything.
B. The man should only take what he needs.
C. The man shouldn't take his cell phone.

**3.** A. The man should include all his information.
B. The man's résumé can be more than a page.
C. The man shouldn't write too much.

## LISTENING II

***(Tracks 14–16)* You will hear the first part of a conversation. To finish the conversation, listen and choose the correct answer: A, B, or C.**

**4.** A. Sure, of course.
B. No, thank you.
C. Yes, could I?

**5.** A. I'd like to give my supervisor two weeks' notice.
B. I work in a clothing store, and I'm studying retail management.
C. I'm working hard to improve my communication skills.

**6.** A. Yes. What would my typical workday be like?
B. No, we haven't made a decision yet.
C. Yes. Why are you leaving your current job?

## LISTENING III

***(Tracks 17–18)* You will hear a conversation. Then you will hear three sentences. Which sentence is true: A, B, or C?**

**7.** A. The man doesn't have a job now.
B. The man is a stock clerk now.
C. The man works at a supermarket now.

**8.** A. The man has gotten a lot of work experience.
B. The man has some job training.
C. The man has gotten a new job.

NAME ____________________

## LIFE SKILLS

### Read the next page and answer these questions. What is the correct answer: A, B, C, or D?

**9.** Based on its organization, what type of résumé is this?

A. a chronological résumé

B. a functional résumé

C. an educational résumé

D. a professional résumé

**10.** What information did Alvaro *not* include in his résumé?

A. his contact information

B. his work experience

C. his educational background

D. names of his references

**11.** What does Alvaro do now?

A. He's the assistant manager of a hotel.

B. He's a front desk clerk.

C. He's a restaurant manager.

D. He's a student.

**12.** What does Alvaro's experience *not* include?

A. working as a hotel manager

B. providing customer service

C. organizing records

D. hiring employees

**13.** What information should Alvaro add to this résumé?

A. his date of birth

B. his employment history

C. his skills

D. how much money he makes

**Alvaro Camacho**
**2938 H St., Apt. 1A, Alexandria, VA 22305**
**Phone: 703-555-2981**
**E-mail: a_camacho@washingtondcmail.com**

| | | |
|---|---|---|
| **Position Desired** | Seeking a full-time hotel assistant manager position. | |
| **Experience** | **2008–present** | **Covington Hotel, Washington D.C.**<br>*Front Desk Clerk*<br>Organize and maintain reservations and other records. Provide excellent customer service, including responding to customer questions, requests, and complaints. Handle guest reservations by phone and in person. Provide guests with smooth registration, payment, and checkout processes. |
| | **2005–2008** | **Lotus Restaurant, Washington D.C.**<br>*Manager*<br>Hired and trained new employees. Managed five employees. Prepared workers' schedules. Organized and maintained records of orders and supplies. |
| **Education** | **2007–2008** | **Metro Technical School, Washington D.C.**<br>One-year certificate in hotel and restaurant management |
| | **2005–2006** | **New Adult School, Shirlington, VA**<br>Classes: ESL, computers, culinary arts |
| **References** | Provided upon request. | |
| **Transcripts** | Provided upon request. | |

NAME________________________________

## GRAMMAR

### Complete each conversation. What is the correct answer: A, B, or C?

**14. A:** Tell me a little about your work experience.
**B:** Right now I work in a factory. I ______ there since last year.

A. worked
B. 'm working
C. 've worked

**15. A:** Is Ivan ready for his job interview tomorrow?
**B:** Yes, everything is done. His suit is ironed, and he ______ copies of his résumé. He has 20 copies.

A. was making
B. 's made
C. has been making

**16. A:** After your interview, did the company check your references?
**B:** Yes, yesterday they ______ my supervisor.

A. called
B. have called
C. were calling

**17. A:** Have ______ on any interviews recently?
**B:** Yes, I had one last week with a new software company.

A. you went
B. you gone
C. you go

**18. A:** Are you finished with your résumé?
**B:** Almost. A friend has ______ me, but I'm not done yet.

A. been helping
B. helping
C. been helped

**19. A:** How are you?
**B:** I'm fine, but I'm really tired. ______, and I'm not getting enough sleep!

A. I took night classes
B. I've been taking night classes
C. I've taken night classes

**20. A:** Eric is really trying to find a job. He ______ to the career center every day for a week.
**B:** Well, I hope he finds something soon.

A. has been going
B. has gone
C. Both A and B are correct.

NAME ____________________

# READING I

**Read the next page and answer these questions. What is the correct answer: A, B, C, or D?**

**21.** What is the purpose of this information?

A. to help a person prepare answers to interview questions

B. to help a person prepare to interview someone for a job

C. to give tips on good nonverbal communication for an interview

D. to explain how to understand nonverbal communication in an interview

**22.** Which of the following is an example of nonverbal communication?

A. asking an interviewer questions

B. smiling and looking a person in the eye

C. giving good answers to an interviewer's questions

D. using correct grammar

**23.** How is verbal communication different from nonverbal communication?

A. You can send messages only with verbal communication, not with nonverbal communication.

B. Verbal communication skills are always more essential than nonverbal skills.

C. Interviewers use verbal communication, while the people they interview use nonverbal communication.

D. Much of nonverbal communication is visual.

**24.** Which of the following does the article recommend?

A. covering the smell of cigarette smoke with cologne or perfume

B. letting your cell phone ring if you get a call during an interview

C. nodding your head to show interest while the interviewer talks

D. tapping your fingers to help you feel less nervous

**25.** Which of the following should you do during an interview?

A. throw away your gum

B. prepare answers to common interview questions

C. think about the interviewer's nonverbal skills

D. look at the interviewer

# Send the Right Message

Before an interview, it's essential to prepare and practice answers to common job interview questions. However, studies show that less than half of communication is verbal, or spoken. People's appearance and behavior send a very strong message to others. So it's also important—maybe even *more* important—to think about and be aware of your nonverbal communication skills. Here are some tips to help you send the right nonverbal message.

Before the interview, choose clothing that is appropriate for the job you're interviewing for. It should not be too casual. For example, it's usually better for men to wear a button-down shirt, slacks, and shoes instead of a T-shirt, jeans, and sneakers. Your clothes should always be clean, pressed, and in good condition. Make sure your hair is neat and clean. Keep your fingernails short, neat, and clean. Wear little or no jewelry. Women should wear only light makeup. Use little or no cologne or perfume, and don't smoke before an interview. Turn off your cell phone, and throw away gum, drinks, and food ahead of time.

When you meet the interviewer, give a firm handshake, smile, look the person in the eye, and introduce yourself. During the interview, try to look calm. Don't tap your fingers, touch your hair, or make other nervous movements. Sit up straight, and keep both feet on the floor and your hands in your lap. Make eye contact and nod your head as the interviewer talks to show that you're interested. Always pay attention to what the interviewer is saying.

# READING II

## Read the next page and answer these questions. What is the correct answer: A, B, C, or D?

**26.** What is the main idea of the article?

A. It's normal to feel nervous for a job interview.

B. There are different ways to help yourself reduce nervousness about an interview.

C. Practicing interview questions is a good way to feel less nervous and to do better at an interview.

D. It's very important to give good answers to job interview questions.

**27.** Which is true about the questions in the article?

A. They are good questions to ask an interviewer.

B. They are commonly asked in interviews.

C. You'll always have to answer these questions in any job interview.

D. There is only one correct answer to each of the questions.

**28.** How are the sample answers to questions 1 and 2 similar?

A. They both explain that the person's skills can help the company.

B. They both include examples of the person's skills.

C. They both focus on the kind of job the person wants.

D. They both include suggestions for the company.

**29.** According to the article, which sentence is true?

A. A short answer to a question is probably better than a long one.

B. It's probably better to have only one method of preparing for a job interview.

C. The interviewer will probably know if you're very nervous.

D. If you're less nervous, your interview will probably go better.

**30.** What advice is given for talking about your present job?

A. Explain why you're good at your job.

B. Don't talk a lot about your job.

C. Don't talk about why your job is bad.

D. Say that you need more responsibility.

## Prepare Yourself:

# Practice Answering Job Interview Questions

It's natural to be nervous about a job interview. But there are ways to reduce your nervousness and to have a better interview. One method is to think about and practice answers to typical job interview questions before your interview. Look at the questions below.

**Question 1:** What is your greatest strength?

**Advice:** Talk about strengths that are related to the job you're applying for, such as your ability to work well with others, your problem-solving skills, or your positive attitude.

**Sample Answer:** *I'm very good with people, and I work well in a team. I believe my excellent problem-solving skills can make a difference in this company.*

**Question 2:** Why do you want to work here?

**Advice:** Talk about what you can do for the company. Relate your interests and abilities to the company's needs.

**Sample Answer:** *This company is a place where I can make a difference. I think I'd be able to use my skills to make important contributions to the company for a long time.*

**Question 3:** What do you dislike about your present job?

**Advice:** Don't say anything negative. Focus on the positive things that you want from your next job, such as more responsibility, a chance to move up in the company, or an opportunity to work in a certain field.

**Sample Answer:** *I enjoy my present job. But I'm looking for more of a challenge—a position where I can use my technical knowledge as well as my interpersonal skills.*

## WRITING

### Read the next page and answer these questions. What is the correct answer: A, B, C, or D?

**31.** When Delia writes a cover letter, how should she show that she is a good match for this job?

A. She should list all the job qualifications and requirements.

B. She should include all the key points of her résumé.

C. She should write about her best character traits.

D. She should use some of the language from the job ad to point out her qualifications.

**32.** Which of the following is a key point that Delia should highlight in a cover letter responding to this job ad?

A. She is looking for a full-time job.

B. She would like to receive training.

C. She has experience in customer service.

D. She can provide her transcripts if necessary.

**33.** The following is part of a paragraph from Delia's cover letter. Which sentence best completes the paragraph with information about her skills?

> **As you can see in my attached résumé, I have recently completed my education at Frontera Technical School and received a computer support specialist certificate. ________________________________. I have developed strong communication and customer service skills and gained training experience in my current job as a supermarket manager.**

A. I am good at problem-solving and have excellent interpersonal skills.

B. Because I have worked as a computer support specialist, I am a good match for your company's needs.

C. In my job now, I often work with customers.

D. I am an ideal candidate for the position because I am hardworking and dependable.

**Computer Support Specialist**

Linea Communications is looking for a dependable, hardworking, motivated individual to join our team. The ideal candidate possesses good interpersonal skills, communicates effectively, and can handle customer-service complaints professionally. Experience training others, strong organizational skills, and attention to detail are required. Related experience and/or education is a plus.

**Delia Gonzalez**

293 South Vista Ave., Apt. 3C, San Diego, CA 92109
Phone: 760-555-4213 E-mail: dgonzalez@wow.com

**Position Desired** Seeking a full-time position as a computer support specialist.

**Experience**

**2007–present** **Tere's Taco Shack, San Diego, CA**
*Manager*
Provide excellent customer service, including responding to customer complaints. Organize and maintain records of orders and supplies. Manage seven employees per shift. Train new employees.

**2004–2007** **San Diego International Airport, San Diego, CA**
*Baggage handler*
Operated luggage cart, scissor-lift truck, and forklift. Paid great attention to detail to ensure correct locations of bags.

**Education**

**2006–2007** **Frontera Technical School, San Diego, CA**
Received computer support specialist certificate.

**2004–2005** **Santa Maria Community Adult School, San Diego, CA**
Classes: ESL, computers.

**References** Provided upon request

**Transcripts** Provided upon request

NAME________________________________________

# Unit 3 Test

## LISTENING I

***(Tracks 19–21 )* You will hear a question. Then you will hear a conversation. After that, you will hear the question again and three choices. What is the correct answer: A, B, or C?**

**1.** A. pulling over to the shoulder
B. waiting in the car
C. getting help from other drivers

**2.** A. take Morgan Street
B. cross the Morgan Street Bridge
C. take a detour

**3.** A. how to keep a car in good condition
B. where you can find out about traffic problems
C. what to do if you're having car trouble

## LISTENING II

***(Tracks 22–23)* You will hear the first part of a conversation. To finish the conversation, listen and choose the correct answer: A, B, or C.**

**4.** A. Yeah, but the engine needs some oil.
B. Yeah, but my windshield wipers don't work.
C. Yeah, but I didn't step on the accelerator.

**5.** A. In the trunk.
B. Under the hood.
C. On the dashboard.

## LISTENING III

***(Tracks 24–26)* You will hear a conversation. Then you will hear three sentences. Which sentence is true: A, B, or C?**

**6.** A. The woman called someone to help her.
B. A police officer helped her change the tire.
C. The woman got a ride with her friend.

**7.** A. The man's car is at the mechanic's.
B. The man's car isn't running well.
C. The man wants to get the oil changed in his car.

**8.** A. The woman is going to drive across the bridge.
B. The bridge is closed to pedestrians.
C. The woman can walk across the bridge.

NAME ____________________

# LIFE SKILLS I

**Read. What is the correct answer: A, B, C, or D?**

Parisa was backing up her car when she accidentally hit another vehicle. Parisa's car was fine, but the bill to repair the damage to the other vehicle was $1,500. Fortunately, she had property damage liability insurance, so her insurance company paid part of the costs. But first she had to pay her deductible—$1,000.

**9.** Look at the picture. Which part of the car was damaged?

A. the taillight

B. the windshield

C. the trunk

D. the bumper

**10.** Which sentence is true?

A. Parisa's insurance company paid the full cost of fixing the other vehicle.

B. Parisa paid for part of the costs to repair the other vehicle.

C. Parisa's insurance didn't cover damage to the other driver's vehicle.

D. Parisa's insurance company paid only for the damage to Parisa's car.

**11.** How much money did Parisa's insurance pay to repair the vehicle?

A. $500

B. $1,000

C. $1,500

D. $2,500

# LIFE SKILLS II

## Look at the map Selena used to go to a concert in Memorial Park. Then answer these questions. What is the correct answer: A, B, C, or D?

**Driving directions to 1649 W Adams St, Phoenix, AZ 85007**
**2.6 mi** ~ about **8 mins**

**1350 S 27th Ave, Phoenix, AZ 85009**

1. Head **north** on **S 27th Ave** toward **W Buckeye Rd**
2. Turn **right** at **W Buckeye Rd**
3. Turn **left** at **S 19th Ave**
4. Turn **right** at **W Jefferson St**
5. Turn **left** at **S 15th Ave**
6. Turn **left** at **W Washington St**
7. Continue on **W Washington St**
   Destination will be on the right

**1649 W Washington St, Phoenix, AZ 85007**

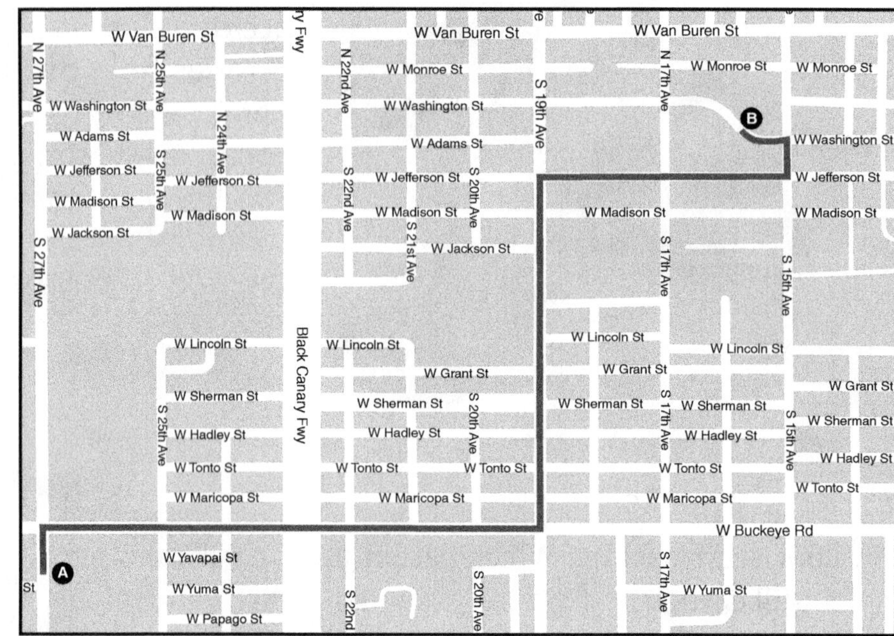


12. On the route from Selena's home (A) to Memorial Park (B), which road crosses the Black Canyon Fwy?
    A. S 27th Ave.
    B. W Buckeye Rd.
    C. S 19th Ave.
    D. W Van Buren St.

13. Selena heard on the radio that there was a traffic accident on W Buckeye Rd. Both eastbound lanes on that road are closed. How will this affect her plans?
    A. It won't affect her plans because she won't be traveling on W Buckeye Rd.
    B. It won't affect her plans because she'll be traveling westbound on W Buckeye Rd.
    C. She can't get to the park.
    D. She can take this alternate route: Go northbound on S 27th Ave., then turn right and head east on W Washington St.

NAME ________________________________

## GRAMMAR

### Complete each conversation. What is the correct answer: A, B, or C?

**14. A:** Uh-oh. The check engine light just ________.

**B:** It's OK. We'll get off at the next exit and see what the problem is.

A. came on
B. came on it
C. Both A and B are correct.

**15. A:** What happened to your car door? The paint is scratched.

**B:** I know. I accidentally ________ with a shopping cart at the supermarket.

A. ran it into
B. ran into it
C. Both A and B are correct.

**16. A:** Why do have your headlights on? It's still daylight.

**B:** I know. I always ________ because they help other cars see me.

A. turn them on
B. turn on them
C. Both A and B are correct.

**17. A:** I'd like to ________ at the bus station. Can I borrow your car?

**B:** Well, I don't think I need it, but let me check my schedule.

A. pick up my sister
B. pick my sister up
C. Both A and B are correct.

**18. A:** It's so dangerous ________ on the phone while you're driving.

**B:** I know. I rarely use a phone in the car, even with a headset.

A. to talk
B. talking
C. Both A and B are correct.

**19. A:** My car battery died last night in the parking lot at school. My brother had to bring jumper cables and jump-start my battery.

**B:** That happened to me once, and I learned a lesson: It's important ________ jumper cables in your car.

A. keeping
B. to keep
C. Both A and B are correct.

**20. A:** I need to get car insurance, but I don't know what kinds I need. Can you help me?

**B:** Sure. ________ the right kinds of coverage is really important.

A. To get
B. Getting
C. Both A and B are correct.

# READING I

## Read the next page and answer these questions. What is the correct answer: A, B, C, or D?

**21.** What is the purpose of this article?

A. to convince people to buy more car insurance

B. to explain how much car insurance costs

C. to provide some general information about car insurance

D. to teach people how to get car insurance

**22.** Read this paraphrase of one of the paragraphs in the article. Which paragraph in the article does it paraphrase?

*Car insurance can protect you. Here's how it works: Every month you pay an insurance company. The insurance company gives you protection—if you have a car accident, the company will pay some or all of the costs of your medical bills and car repairs.*

A. paragraph 2

B. paragraph 3

C. paragraph 4

D. paragraph 5

**23.** Which kind of insurance can help you pay doctors' bills for injuries to yourself that result from a car accident?

A. liability insurance for bodily injury

B. liability insurance for property damage

C. personal injury protection

D. comprehensive coverage

**24.** If you have collision insurance, which of the following is true?

A. Your insurance company will pay for all of the medical bills of anyone who is injured in an accident.

B. Your insurance company will pay for a new car if your car gets stolen.

C. Your insurance company will pay only for damages to other drivers' cars.

D. Your insurance company will pay for repairs if your car gets damaged in an accident.

**25.** Read the article again. What inference can you make?

A. It is legal to drive without car insurance in 47 states.

B. More expensive insurance companies offer better protection than cheaper companies.

C. If you have a lower deductible, you probably have to pay more to the insurance company each month.

D. There are usually no additional costs to get greater amounts of coverage.

## The Basics of Car Insurance

❶ The laws of 47 states require car owners to have insurance. But buying car insurance can be confusing. Here is some basic information that all car owners should know.

❷ Car insurance is protection. When you get car insurance, you pay an insurance company a certain amount of money, usually each month. The insurance company gives you coverage—if you're in a car accident, the company pays all or part of the costs, such as medical bills and car repairs.

❸ A deductible is an amount of money that you are responsible for paying after an accident. For example, if you're in an accident that causes $3,000 worth of damage and your deductible is $500, you must pay $500, and the insurance company will pay the balance of $2,500. You can choose how much you want your deductible to be. If you want to pay less for insurance each month, you can choose to have a higher deductible.

❹ There are different types of car insurance. Most states require drivers to have liability insurance for bodily injury and property damage. These types of insurance pay for injuries to *others* and/or damage to *their* property. Some states require personal injury protection (PIP), too. This type of insurance pays for *your* medical expenses resulting from an auto accident. Collision coverage pays for damage to *your* car from an auto accident. Comprehensive coverage pays for loss of or damage to your car that doesn't happen in an auto accident (for example, damage due to theft or a flood).

❺ Each state requires different minimum amounts of liability insurance (and sometimes other kinds). Insurance companies can tell you what the minimums are in your state, and then you decide if you want to buy more. Think carefully before you choose the amount of coverage you want. A higher amount of coverage means that you pay more each month. A lower amount of coverage means that you pay less each month, but the insurance company won't pay as much if you have an accident. And remember—you're responsible for paying whatever costs the company doesn't pay.

# READING II

## Read the next page and answer these questions. What is the correct answer: A, B, C, or D?

**26.** What is the purpose of this article?

A. to give an example of why car insurance is important

B. to explain how to get information from other drivers

C. to explain why drivers should report accidents to their insurance companies

D. to give an example of what to do after a car accident

**27.** What happened to Chi's car?

A. Another driver hit it with her car.

B. It was damaged in the accident.

C. Chi wasn't able to drive it after the accident.

D. It was fixed by the insurance company.

**28.** What did Chi do after exchanging information with the other driver?

A. He waited for the police to arrive.

B. He took notes about the accident.

C. He made some calls on his cell phone.

D. He checked the weather conditions.

**29.** What did Chi do first after the accident?

A. He looked to see if the cars were damaged.

B. He tried to stop his car.

C. He moved his car to the side of the road.

D. He checked to see if the other driver was hurt.

**30.** Read the article again. What inference can you make?

A. Chi probably had never been in an accident before.

B. The other driver probably developed pain after the accident.

C. Chi probably caused the accident by looking away from the road.

D. The insurance company will probably decide the accident wasn't Chi's fault.

## The Right Steps After an Accident

Chi Yang was on his way to work one morning. As he slowed down at a traffic light, his cell phone rang. Chi looked down to see who it was. But when he looked up again, the car in front of him had stopped. Chi stepped on the brakes, but he didn't have enough time to stop before he hit the car.

Chi pulled his car over to the shoulder, and so did the other driver. They both turned off their cars and got out. Neither of the drivers seemed to have any injuries, so next they checked the cars for damage. The bumper of Chi's car had a dent, and one of the headlights was broken. The paint on the other car was scratched, and the rear bumper was dented.

Then Chi asked the other driver for her name, address, and phone number, and he wrote down this information. He also made note of her insurance information, her driver's license number, and the license plate number of her car. Next Chi wrote down all the details of the accident. He wrote everything he remembered, including the time, weather conditions, and exactly what happened. His cell phone had a camera on it, so he used it to take pictures of the damage to both cars. Finally, he called his insurance company and the police to report the accident. He gave them all the information he could, including the notes he took about the details of the accident.

There is one thing that Chi didn't do: He didn't say the accident was his fault. This is important. It's the job of the police and the drivers' insurance companies, not the drivers, to decide who is responsible for an accident.

NAME ________________________________

## WRITING

### Read the next page and answer these questions. What is the correct answer: A, B, C, or D?

**31.** Which sentence best completes the first paragraph by clearly stating the argument?

A. DUI is dangerous, and there should be tougher punishments for people who do it.

B. Not enough people know about the danger of driving under the influence.

C. There are many ways that you can help stop friends and family from driving under the influence.

D. The U.S. government reports that there are fewer accidents related to driving under the influence than there were ten years ago.

**32.** Which of the following is a specific detail that supports the argument in the second paragraph?

A. Many people don't believe that their reaction times are reduced by drugs or alcohol.

B. Studies have been done to measure the reaction times of drivers when they're under the influence.

C. Driving when you're very tired is also dangerous because it can also reduce your reaction time.

D. Studies show that it takes drivers about two seconds longer to react to different road situations when they are under the influence.

**33.** Which sentence in the fourth paragraph does *not* support the argument and therefore should be deleted?

A. Driving under the influence is a serious crime that deserves tough punishment.

B. We need stronger DUI laws.

C. Stronger laws will help keep our roads safe for responsible drivers.

D. I never drink and drive, and I encourage my friends and family not to either.

## Letter to the Editor:

Driving under the influence (DUI) refers to driving after drinking alcohol or taking certain drugs. ____________ (31.). This would help make our roads safer for everyone.

One reason that driving under the influence is dangerous is that it reduces your reaction time, or the time it takes you to respond to something you see or hear. ____________ (32.). This might not seem like a big difference. But if something happens suddenly —which is always a possibility while driving—it could mean the difference between life and death.

Another reason why driving under the influence is dangerous is that it doesn't just affect the person who drives. Every year drivers under the influence cause thousands of accidents that take the lives of innocent people.

Driving under the influence is a serious crime that deserves tough punishment. We need stronger DUI laws. Stronger laws will help keep our roads safe for responsible drivers. I never drink and drive, and I encourage my friends and family not to either.

**Kari Chopra**

**Paramus, New Jersey**

NAME ______________________________

# Unit 4 Test

## LISTENING I

**(*Tracks 27–29*) You will hear a question. Then you will hear a conversation. After that, you will hear the question again and three choices. What is the correct answer: A, B, or C?**

**1.** A. He goes to a babysitter's house.
B. He's at home alone.
C. He does after-school activities.

**2.** A. an earthquake survivor
B. a police officer
C. a rescuer

**3.** A. call 911
B. call the neighbor
C. call her mother at work

## LISTENING II

**(*Tracks 30–31*) You will hear the first part of a conversation. To finish the conversation, listen and choose the correct answer: A, B, or C.**

**4.** A. A tornado has been reported.
B. There could be a tornado soon.
C. We should take shelter immediately.

**5.** A. You should get window guards.
B. You should get electrical outlet covers.
C. It's a good idea to have some emergency supplies.

## LISTENING III

**(*Tracks 32–34*) You will hear a conversation. Then you will hear three sentences. Which sentence is true: A, B, or C?**

**6.** A. Many people were injured.
B. There were no injuries.
C. There were no survivors.

**7.** A. The woman put gas in the car.
B. The man didn't put gas in the car.
C. They don't need to get gas.

**8.** A. There's a hazard in the workplace.
B. Mr. Chen has fixed the hazard.
C. The woman is going to file a complaint with OSHA.

NAME ____________________

## LIFE SKILLS

### Read the questions. What is the correct answer: A, B, C, or D?

**9.** What is the purpose of skid-resistant flooring?

A. to make it easy to clean up spills

B. to make sure that the floor is even

C. to help people avoid slipping and falling

D. to reduce injuries resulting from standing for long periods of time

**10.** What is the purpose of doorstops and door holders?

A. to keep children from opening a closed door

B. to keep doors from closing on children's fingers

C. to keep children from opening cabinet doors

D. to keep doors closed so children don't go into unsafe areas

**11.** What is the purpose of worker safety equipment?

A. to give workers a way to report dangers in the workplace

B. to warn workers about workplace hazards

C. to prevent workers from getting injured

D. to provide workers with a list of safety tips

**12.** How can parents reduce the dangers of electrical shock to children?

A. use a safety gate to block all outlets

B. make sure there is enough light

C. unplug all electrical appliances

D. put outlet covers over all outlets

**13.** Which product could keep a child out of unsafe areas and prevent him or her from falling down stairs?

A. a latch

B. a safety gate

C. skid-resistant shoes

D. a window guard

NAME ____________________

## GRAMMAR

### Complete each conversation. What is the correct answer: A, B, or C?

**14. A:** Some of the workers in the Chem-All factory are suffering from health problems because of dangerous chemicals that were kept there. The employees knew about the chemicals, but they were afraid to complain.

**B:** That's too bad. They ________ the problem to OSHA without even giving their names.

A. could have reported
B. might not have reported
C. should have been reported

**15. A:** How's your family after the hurricane? Is everyone OK?

**B:** Luckily, yes. But we didn't evacuate, and that was a bad idea. We ________ when government officials told us to.

A. could have left
B. may have left
C. should have left

**16. A:** My mom and dad both worked when I was young, so my brother and I were latchkey kids.

**B:** Really? I guess you were good kids. My grandmother watched my sister and me because my mom knew we ________ into a lot of trouble without an adult around.

A. might have gotten
B. should have gotten
C. could not have gotten

**17. A:** Don't blame yourself for your niece's accident. It wasn't your fault.

**B:** Yes it was! I was supposed to be watching her, and she ________, even for a second.

A. may not have been left alone
B. might not have been left alone
C. shouldn't have been left alone

**18. A:** What are you reading?

**B:** It's a news story about the rescue efforts after the earthquake. Rescuers are still searching for survivors. People ________ under rubble when buildings fell.

A. could have trapped
B. may have been trapped
C. might have trapped

**19. A:** I can't believe so many of my important papers were ruined in the flood.

**B:** Yeah, it's too bad you didn't keep them in a waterproof container. They ________ if you'd done that.

A. shouldn't have been ruined
B. might not have been ruined
C. may have been ruined

**20. A:** Did you hear that Esteban slipped and fell at work? I don't know how it happened, though.

**B:** I heard the floor was wet. He ________ to wear his skid-resistant shoes.

A. might not have forgotten
B. could not have forgotten
C. may have forgotten

NAME ______________________

# READING I

**Read the next page and answer these questions. What is the correct answer: A, B, C, or D?**

**21.** What is the main idea of the article?

A. Packing is the most important part of planning for an evacuation.

B. To prepare for evacuation you should 1) pack the things you will need, and 2) plan where to go and how to get there.

C. In case of evacuation it's essential for each family member to have identification and copies of important documents.

D. Before you evacuate you should think about two options: staying with friends or family or going to a shelter.

**22.** When can you go back to your home after an evacuation?

A. as soon as the natural disaster is over

B. three days later

C. when officials say it's safe

D. after several days

**23.** Read the article again. What inference can you make?

A. You should be prepared in case there is no electricity during or after an emergency.

B. Your cell phone probably won't work after a natural disaster or emergency.

C. If you're well prepared for an evacuation, you can leave your home later.

D. If you have three people in your family, you only need to pack food for one day.

**24.** Read the article again. What inference can you make?

A. One person in each family should be in charge of packing for everyone.

B. Shelters don't usually provide pillows and blankets.

C. It's safer to stay in a shelter than with a friend or family member.

D. It's better to take public transportation than to drive during an evacuation.

**25.** Which sentence best summarizes the last section of the article (the section beginning with "Once you know where you'll stay...")?

A. Think about what kind of transportation you'll use and what route you'll take to evacuate.

B. After you choose where you're going, decide whether you'll take public transportation or drive.

C. It's a good idea to evacuate as early as possible to avoid traffic.

D. Be patient because many other people will be on the roads at the same time as you.

# Evacuation Preparation

During or after some natural disasters and emergencies, it's not safe to stay in your home. If that's the case, you should evacuate, or leave your home, until officials say it's safe to return. If you have to evacuate, you probably won't have a lot of time to pack. So you should always have ready some basic things that you'll need while you're away from home.

- Pack enough water and food for everyone in your family for at least three days.
- You'll need a battery-powered radio to get information and instructions. Also, make sure you have a cell phone to communicate with family and friends.
- Pack extra clothes for each person—you may be gone for a few days. Prepare a first-aid kit to take care of anyone who gets hurt or sick. Include disinfectant wipes to keep things clean. Take personal items such as prescription medication, a toothbrush, toothpaste, and, if necessary, baby and pet supplies. Also include a flashlight and extra batteries. If you're going to a shelter, you should pack pillows and blankets, too.
- Gather identification, such as birth certificates, passports, and/or social security cards for each family member. Also, make copies of important documents, including your insurance information, bank account records, medical records, and children's school records.

In addition to packing, it's essential to make other evacuation plans.

- You should decide where you'll go if you have to evacuate. One option might be to stay with a friend or family member who lives outside of the evacuation area. In addition, many cities have shelters where people can stay during an evacuation. Pet owners: Many shelters don't accept pets, so make other plans for your animals if necessary.
- Once you know where you'll stay when you evacuate, think about how you'll get there if you need to. Some cities offer public transportation to evacuation shelters. You should know how and where to get this transportation. If you have a car, find out about evacuation routes in your area and plan the route you'll take. Many other people will probably be evacuating at the same time, so expect long lines for public transportation and a lot of traffic on the roads.

## READING II

**Read the next page and answer these questions. What is the correct answer: A, B, C, or D?**

**26.** What is the main idea of this news story?

A. Charlie and Shelly Kerns survived a tornado in an amazing way.

B. After a tornado took their home, Charlie and Shelly Kerns planned to be prepared the next time a storm hits.

C. Charlie and Shelly Kerns are grateful for learning a lesson about how dangerous tornadoes can be.

D. Charlie and Shelly Kerns are thankful after a storm left them without a house, but with each other.

**27.** What happened first?

A. The windows broke.

B. The floor lifted up.

C. Kerns got to the basement safely.

D. Kerns covered his head.

**28.** How did Charlie Kerns get injured?

A. He was injured when he fell on the floor.

B. He got cut when he broke the glass.

C. He got hit by objects flying around in the storm.

D. He was trapped under the rubble of his home.

**29.** Read the news story again. What inference can you make?

A. Shelly Kerns wishes she hadn't gone to work the night of the tornado.

B. Charlie Kerns hadn't heard about a tornado watch before he heard about the tornado warning.

C. Charlie decided not to go to the basement because he wanted to watch the storm.

D. In the future, Charlie Kerns will always have emergency supplies in his home.

**30.** Which of the following is the best summary of the second paragraph of the news story?

A. Shelly Kerns and her husband survived the storm, but their house didn't. Still, Shelly is very grateful that she still has her husband and her job at the hospital.

B. Shelly Kerns was helping people who had gotten hurt in the storm. Even though her husband had injuries of his own, somehow she knew he would be OK.

C. Because she works in a hospital, Shelly Kerns had seen people survive terrible disasters. So even though her house was destroyed by a tornado, she thought her husband was alive.

D. Shelly Kerns was at work when she learned that her house had been destroyed by a tornado. She knew her husband had been in the house. It didn't make sense, but she believed that her husband had survived the storm.

# An Amazing Story Of Survival

It was a calm and quiet evening in northern Tennessee. Charlie Kerns was relaxing and watching TV when suddenly a tornado warning flashed onto the screen. Kerns immediately headed for the safest place in his house—the basement. He was on his way when he heard the sound of glass breaking. All of a sudden, he felt like the floor was lifting under him. He immediately lay down on the floor and covered his head with his hands and arms. Kerns heard a lot of noise and felt tremendous pressure. For several minutes, furniture and pieces of the house itself flew around him, hitting his arms, back, and legs. Then, suddenly, everything was quiet. Kerns slowly lifted his head and looked around. He saw that he was lying on the ground. The floor under him was gone. So was his entire house! There was nothing left at all. Kerns checked himself. His body was sore, and his arm was bleeding. But he was alive!

Kerns's wife Shelly was working at her job at Memorial Hospital when the tornado hit. After the storm, Shelly was helping patients who had been injured when she got the news that her house had been destroyed. Shelly knew her husband had been at home that evening, and she knew there was no way he could have survived that storm. But for some reason, Shelly refused to believe that her husband was dead. She just felt that he was OK. And, of course, she was right.

That was three days ago. The Kerns are living in temporary housing, and probably will be for a while. Their only belongings are the clothes they're wearing. But they feel grateful and remain optimistic. Mrs. Kerns said, "We have each other, and that's the most important thing."

NAME______________________

## WRITING

### Read the next page and answer these questions. What is the correct answer: A, B, C, or D?

**31.** Which of the following introductory paragraphs best communicates the topic of the article?

A. It's every parent's responsibility to make sure that his or her home is safe for children. Children are hurt in the kitchen more often than adults.

B. The kitchen and bathrooms are the most dangerous rooms in the home. More than half of home injuries happen in one of these two rooms.

C. More injuries happen in the kitchen than in any other room. But most of these injuries can easily be prevented.

D. Fires are a big danger in the kitchen. It's important to know how to prevent fires and to know what to do if there is a fire.

**32.** Which of the following best completes the second sentence of the next paragraph by providing a clear instruction?

A. Never walk away

B. You don't walk away

C. You shouldn't have walked away

D. If you never walk away

**33.** Which of the following signal words best connects the last paragraph to the ones before it?

A. Third

B. After

C. Later

D. Finally

## How to Make Your Kitchen Safer

__________
31.

To start with, one of the most important things you can do is to prevent fires. __________ (32.) from food cooking on the stove. Keep anything that could catch on fire, such as towels, pot holders, and curtains, at least three feet from the stove. Clothing can catch on fire, too. When cooking, don't wear loose clothing, and be sure to roll up your sleeves. Buy a fire extinguisher. Learn how to use it, and keep it nearby.

Next, take action to avoid burns. Turn the handles of hot pots and pans toward the back of the stove so they can't be grabbed by a child or accidentally bumped and spilled. Also, be careful when taking lids off hot pots or microwaveable containers. Escaping steam is hotter than boiling water and can cause serious burns.

If you have children, be sure to reduce their risk of accidental poisoning. Keep chemicals and cleaning products locked in a cabinet. Even if you don't have children, beware—household products can be dangerous for adults, too, if they're not used properly. Always read the label before using any household product.

__________ (33.), use caution to prevent cuts. Keep knives out of reach of children. If you break something such as a glass or plate, clean it up quickly. Small pieces can be very sharp and can cause painful cuts.

**by Rusmir Klickovic**

NAME ______________________________

# Unit 5 Test

## LISTENING I

**_(Tracks 35–37)_ You will hear a question. Then you will hear a conversation. After that, you will hear the question again and three choices. What is the correct answer: A, B, or C?**

**1.** A. He'll take some classes.
B. He'll leave his job.
C. He'll ask about his performance review.

**2.** A. get some training at work
B. tell his boss he's ready for more responsibility
C. ask his boss about on-the-job training

**3.** A. The man makes mistakes.
B. The man doesn't finish his work on time.
C. The man has a negative attitude.

## LISTENING II

**_(Tracks 38–39)_ You will hear the first part of a conversation. To finish the conversation, listen and choose the correct answer: A, B, or C.**

**4.** A. Yes, it's a long shot on this one.
B. Yes, Mike calls the shots on this one.
C. Yes, Mike has two strikes against him on this one.

**5.** A. Thanks. I'll be on time from now on.
B. Thank you. That was nice of you.
C. OK. I'll work on that.

## LISTENING III

**_(Tracks 40–42)_ You will hear a conversation. Then you will hear three sentences. Which sentence is true: A, B, or C?**

**6.** A. The man was promoted.
B. The man thinks he probably won't get the job.
C. The man will decide who gets the promotion.

**7.** A. The woman is explaining what she needs.
B. The woman is blaming the man.
C. The woman is bothering the man.

**8.** A. The woman was promoted.
B. The woman has strong communication skills.
C. The woman is interested in taking a course.

NAME________________________________

# LIFE SKILLS

**Read the next page and answer these questions. What is the correct answer: A, B, C, or D?**

**9.** Carmela is interested in getting a higher position in her company, but she needs to get some basic computer training first. Which course should she probably take?

A. Computer Fundamentals

B. Internet Fundamentals

C. E-mail Fundamentals

D. Computers and the Job Search

**10.** What is the reference number of the course that is offered on Monday and Wednesday evenings?

A. 162

B. 252

C. 254

D. 416

**11.** On what days and times is Computer Fundamentals offered?

A. Monday, Wednesday, Friday from 12:00 P.M. to 2:00 P.M. and Tuesday, Thursday, Saturday from 8:00 A.M. to 10:00 A.M.

B. Monday, Wednesday, Friday from 8:00 A.M. to 10:00 A.M. and Tuesday, Thursday, Saturday from 12:00 P.M. to 2:00 P.M.

C. Monday, Wednesday, Friday from 6:00 P.M. to 8:00 P.M. and Tuesday, Thursday, Saturday from 10:00 A.M. to 12:00 P.M.

D. Monday, Wednesday, Friday from 8:00 A.M. to 10:00 A.M. and Tuesday, Thursday, Saturday from 8:00 A.M.to 10:00 A.M.

**12.** What are the reference numbers for the courses that include a weekend class?

A. 162, 163, 255

B. 163, 253, 255

C. 163, 252, 254

D. 163, 253, 417

**13.** Ming works Monday through Friday from 3:00 P.M. to 11:00 P.M. He wants to take Internet Fundamentals and E-mail Fundamentals. Which courses can he take?

A. He can take the courses with reference numbers 252 and 254.

B. He can take the courses with reference numbers 253 and 255.

C. He can take the courses with reference numbers 252 and 255.

D. He can take the courses with reference numbers 253 and 254.

### 162, 163 Computer Fundamentals

Designed for students who want to update their skills to become more employable or to achieve a promotion. Students will develop a basic understanding of computers, both hardware and software. Focuses on essential computer terminology. This course will also include a basic study of MS Word®, MS Excel®, and MS PowerPoint®.

### 254, 255 E-mail Fundamentals

Focuses on e-mail basics. Students will learn to set up a free account, to send and receive messages, to delete and organize messages into folders, to set up an address book, to send and receive attachments, and to follow basic online etiquette.

### 252, 253 Internet Fundamentals

Focus on basic skills needed to use the Internet. Students will learn to set up a home page and to search and access websites, as well as to "surf." Students will become familiar with resources including newspapers, libraries, and local government sites.

### 416, 417 Computers and the Job Search

Strategies for using a computer in a job search, including navigating Internet resources, completing an online application, and attaching a résumé to an e-mail message. Emphasis on résumé and cover-letter writing.

| Reference number | Course title | Meeting days | Time |
|---|---|---|---|
| 162 | Computer Fundamentals | M, W, F | 8:00 A.M.–10:00 A.M. |
| 163 | Computer Fundamentals | T, Th, Sa | 12:00 P.M.–2:00 P.M. |
| 252 | Internet Fundamentals | M, W, F | 6:00 P.M.–8:00 P.M. |
| 253 | Internet Fundamentals | T, Th, Sa | 10:00 A.M.–12:00 P.M. |
| 254 | E-mail Fundamentals | M, W | 3:00 P.M.–5:00 P.M. |
| 255 | E-mail Fundamentals | T, Th | 8:00 A.M.–10:00 A.M. |
| 416 | Computers and the Job Search | M, W | 7:00 P.M.–9:00 P.M. |
| 417 | Computers and the Job Search | Th, Sa | 10:00 A.M.–12:00 P.M. |

NAME ____________________

## GRAMMAR

### Complete each conversation. What is the correct answer: A, B, or C?

**14. A:** _______ I often work long hours. The schedule is really tough.
**B:** Yeah. I heard you've been working a lot lately.

A. I enjoy my job, although
B. Unless I enjoy my job,
C. I enjoy my job unless

**15. A:** _______ there are still some areas in which I could improve.
**B:** So how are you going to improve in those areas?

A. Unless I've made a lot of progress this year,
B. Although I've made a lot of progress this year,
C. I've made a lot of progress this year unless

**16. A:** I'm really nervous about interviewing for jobs.
**B:** I know, but _______ you go on some interviews. And they get easier with practice.

A. you won't get a job unless
B. you won't get a job, unless
C. you won't get a job although

**17. A:** I don't like team projects. I really prefer to work alone.
**B:** I understand, but you won't do well in this job _______. You need to improve your interpersonal skills.

A. although you learn to work with others
B. unless you learn to work with others
C. you learn to work with others although

**18. A:** _______ a pretty good chance of getting the promotion, it's not a slam dunk.
**B:** Well, good luck. I hope you get it.

A. Although I don't have
B. Unless I have
C. Although I have

**19. A:** I'm thinking about your future with this company. _______ you won't get a promotion.
**B:** Do you have any suggestions for what I can do to improve?

A. You improve your communication skills unless
B. You improve your communication skills although
C. Unless you improve your communication skills,

**20. A:** I don't understand why I got a 2 for attendance.
**B:** Well, _______ you often get to work late.

A. although you never miss a day,
B. unless you never miss a day,
C. you never miss a day unless

# READING I

## Read the next page and answer these questions. What is the correct answer: A, B, C, or D?

**21.** What is the main idea of the first paragraph?

A. You're good at your job, but you want a promotion.

B. When you want a new challenge at work, you're ready for a promotion.

C. If you're well qualified, you'll get a promotion.

D. You can help yourself get a job promotion.

**22.** Which of the following does the article recommend?

A. asking your coworkers to help you get a promotion

B. sharing credit with your coworkers for work you did alone

C. doing extra work to show that you're a good employee

D. giving feedback to your coworkers and supervisor

**23.** Which sentence from the third paragraph best states the main idea of that paragraph?

A. Share ideas and information with your coworkers.

B. Focus on your relationships with other employees.

C. Even if you're not in a leadership position, you can offer to train others.

D. Point out examples of your progress and success.

**24.** Read the article again. What can you infer?

A. You should start working in the position you want to show you're good at it.

B. You won't get a job promotion unless you're the best employee.

C. The relationships you build with other employees can help you get ahead.

D. You always need more education or training to get a promotion.

**25.** According to the article, what is one way to show that you're a good candidate for a promotion?

A. Speak with your supervisor only when you have a problem.

B. Show you're a good leader by giving your coworkers new duties.

C. Try to work fewer hours so you have time to get training for the job you want.

D. Get involved in solving problems.

# Help Yourself Get Ahead

You enjoy your job, but you'd like a new challenge and more responsibility. In other words, you're ready for a promotion. So how do you get it? Well, you *don't* have to wait around for your boss to notice all your hard work and to realize that you're ready to move on. Help yourself get the promotion you want and deserve by showing that you're well qualified for the job.

Stand out from the crowd. Punctuality and attendance are mandatory for any job, so just showing up to work on time every day isn't enough to make an impression. Take initiative to solve problems. Take on additional work, even if it means extra time and effort. Be the best employee that you can be.

Focus on your relationships with other employees. Be a strong team member. Share ideas and information with your coworkers. Then be sure to share credit for work done as a group. Also, demonstrate that you can be an effective leader. Even if you're not in a leadership position, you can offer to train others. Of course, it's essential to establish a good relationship with your supervisor. Communicate regularly, making sure he or she knows what you're working on and what you've achieved. Point out examples of your progress and success. Ask for feedback on your work and suggestions on areas in which you might improve.

Take action to get promoted. Identify the duties and responsibilities of the job that you want. Identify any technical knowledge or skills you need to learn in order to do that job, and then find out how to go about getting the training you need. Sometimes you can learn everything you need on the job. Many times supervisors and even coworkers will be happy to teach you if they see that you're interested in learning something. Find out if your company offers training programs. If so, sign up for them. Finally, if you can't learn everything you need to on the job, you might want to consider coursework or training programs outside your workplace.

Remember, you don't have to wait for someone to help you get a promotion. You can start helping yourself now!

NAME ________________

## READING II

**Read the next page and answer these questions. What is the correct answer: A, B, C, or D?**

**26.** What is the main idea of this information?

A. It reviews an employee's performance.

B. It instructs you on how to evaluate other employees' performance.

C. It suggests ways to improve your job performance.

D. It explains what performance reviews are and why they're important.

**27.** What advice is given in the article?

A. Be honest when you review your performance.

B. Rate yourself as highly as possible.

C. Think carefully when you're reviewing someone's performance.

D. Tell your supervisor only about your strengths and achievements.

**28.** What is one purpose of a performance review?

A. to compare the performance of different employees

B. to help employees identify areas in which they could do their jobs better

C. to learn new skills that will be useful on the job

D. to help employees get higher positions in other companies

**29.** Which sentence best states the main idea of the second paragraph?

A. A performance review is a good time to tell your supervisor about your experience on the job.

B. A performance review allows you to evaluate all the skills necessary to do your job.

C. A performance review is a chance to learn how to move ahead in your career.

D. A performance review allows you to examine the ways in which you've improved.

**30.** Read the article again. What inference can you make?

A. Your supervisor probably isn't interested in your review of your own work.

B. If you regularly receive performance reviews, you're more likely to advance in your career.

C. After you get a promotion, you'll probably get better performance reviews.

D. Good performance reviews may help you earn more responsibility at work.

# Performance Reviews

Many American companies use performance reviews to evaluate how well employees are doing their jobs, to identify areas for improvement, and to set future career goals. Performance reviews are handled differently from company to company, but it's likely that you'll start by evaluating your job performance yourself. Then your supervisor will rate your performance as well. After this, you and your supervisor will probably discuss your ratings and your job performance.

It's important to make the most of your performance reviews. They can provide you with valuable opportunities to receive feedback on your work and to build your career. Take time to evaluate yourself carefully. Be honest in identifying your weaknesses as well as your strengths and achievements. When you meet with your supervisor for your review, listen carefully. This is an excellent chance to get your supervisor's opinions and comments on your work, about both things you do well and areas in which you could improve. Talk about specific ways that you can develop and strengthen the skills you need for your job. Then, in your next performance review, you can evaluate how much you were able to improve.

A performance review is also a good time to talk about your future career goals. Whether you'd like to learn to do your job better, take on more responsibility, or get a promotion, you should discuss your goals with your supervisor. He or she can help you make a plan, including getting the necessary experience and training, to help you reach your goals.

Lastly, performance reviews are important because most companies take them into consideration when they make decisions about promotions. Positive performance reviews are often key for advancing in your career.

# WRITING

**Read the next page and answer these questions. What is the correct answer: A, B, C, or D?**

**31.** Look at Keisha's outline. Which of the following should she use as a second example to support her assessment of her strengths?

A. A number of her accomplishments demonstrate her strengths.

B. She was recognized for having the highest monthly output on her team.

C. She wants to take the company's management-training program.

D. She gave herself an "exceeds expectations" rating.

**32.** In her outline, Keisha identified one area in which she'd like to improve. Which of the following should she add as another example of an opportunity for improvement?

A. She has overcome some weaknesses, including improving her communication skills.

B. She wants to gain experience in other production areas in the factory.

C. Her work is always neat, precise, and of very high quality.

D. She is good at organizing her work schedule to meet deadlines.

**33.** In the future, Keisha would like to use her skills to work as a carpenter. In which paragraph should she include that information?

A. paragraph I

B. paragraph II

C. paragraph III

D. paragraph IV

Keisha Wangai—Self-evaluation

I. Introduction and General Self-assessment

A. Work as a production worker

B. Put together pre-cut pieces to make furniture

C. Strengths: excellent time management skills, hand-eye coordination, and attention to detail

II. Accomplishments That Show My Strengths

A. Frequently meet monthly production goals ahead of schedule

B. ____________
31.

C. Have a record of working extra shifts

III. Opportunities for Improvement

A. Would like to learn to use more of the equipment in our factory

B. ____________
32.

IV. Future Goals

A. Take a company management-training course

B. Study carpentry at Green Valley Technical School

NAME ____________________

# Unit 6 Test

## LISTENING I

***(Tracks 43–45)* You will hear a question. Then you will hear a conversation. After that, you will hear the question again and three choices. What is the correct answer: A, B, or C?**

**1.** A. The man has diabetes.
B. The man is at risk for getting diabetes.
C. The man can prevent himself from becoming diabetic.

**2.** A. how to lower her blood pressure
B. how to check her blood pressure
C. what kind of blood pressure medicine to take

**3.** A. He's going to get his cholesterol medication.
B. He's going to get a cholesterol screening.
C. He's taking his mother for a screening.

## LISTENING II

***(Tracks 46–47)* You will hear the first part of a conversation. To finish the conversation, listen and choose the correct answer: A, B, or C.**

**4.** A. You can change your diet.
B. You can take medication.
C. You can have it checked.

**5.** A. Fine, thank you.
B. That's great!
C. Thanks for asking. I feel terrible. My stomach hurts, and I'm nauseous.

## LISTENING III

***(Tracks 48–50)* You will hear a conversation. Then you will hear three sentences. Which sentence is true: A, B, or C?**

**6.** A. The man is going to see an allergist.
B. The man's legs are red and itchy.
C. The doctor says the problem is serious.

**7.** A. The medicine made the woman feel better.
B. The woman should take the medicine once a day.
C. All the woman's medicine is gone.

**8.** A. The man recommends a doctor.
B. The woman needs to make an appointment.
C. The woman is going to see a cardiologist.

NAME ____________________

## LIFE SKILLS

**Read the next page and answer these questions. What is the correct answer: A, B, C, or D?**

**9.** What is the medicine supposed to do?

A. relieve the patient's allergy symptoms

B. help the patient breathe more easily

C. help the patient sleep better

D. stop the patient's pain

**10.** What should the patient avoid?

A. taking the medicine at night

B. taking the medicine with water

C. sleeping after taking the medicine

D. driving after taking the medicine

**11.** What should the patient do if she forgets to take a pill one morning?

A. Take two pills in the evening.

B. Take the pill as soon as she remembers.

C. Take the next dose at the normal time in the normal amount.

D. Call the doctor.

**12.** What is one possible side effect of the medication?

A. a runny nose

B. allergy symptoms

C. feeling tired

D. feeling very thirsty

**13.** When should the patient stop taking the medicine?

A. when she feels better

B. if she has flu symptoms or difficulty breathing

C. if she is sneezing or has watery eyes and a runny nose

D. if she misses two doses

Notes from 1/20 Appointment with Dr. Walker

- Prescription for fexofenadine
- Will help sneezing, watery eyes, and runny nose from allergies.
- Take with water on an empty stomach (30 min. to 1 hour before meals).
- Take 1 pill in A.M. and 1 at night. (If I miss a dose, take it as soon as I remember.)
- Don't drive after taking medicine, especially at first. Might make me sleepy or dizzy.
- Other side effects could be vomiting or headache.
- Alcohol may make side effects worse.
- Don't stop taking the medicine, even if I feel better.
- Stop taking the medicine and call doctor if I get flu symptoms (chills, body aches, cough, etc.) or have trouble breathing.

# GRAMMAR

## Complete each conversation. What is the correct answer: A, B, or C?

**14. A:** Can you tell me _______?
**B:** The most common side effects are nausea and vomiting.

A. what are the side effects of this medicine
B. what the side effects of this medicine are
C. whether the side effects of this medicine are

**15. A:** I feel terrible. My head hurts so much.
**B:** I have some aspirin. I don't know _______, but you can have some if you want it.

A. whether it will help
B. this helps it
C. what will it help

**16. A:** What time is your appointment with the orthopedist?
**B:** Well, the appointment is at 12:00, but I'm not exactly sure _______. So I think I'll leave here at 11:15.

A. where is the office
B. where's the office
C. where the office is

**17. A:** Sometimes people say to me, "Hi, how are you?" But they don't wait for my answer, so I don't know _______ or not.
**B:** Well, you don't have to give a long answer. Just say something like, "Great! How about you?"

A. if I'm supposed to answer
B. am I supposed to answer
C. what am I supposed to answer

**18. A:** Do you know _______ to the neurologist?
**B:** Yeah. She's been having pain in her arms and hands for a long time.

A. why Melia is going
B. what is Melia going
C. where is Melia going

**19. A:** Could you tell me _______?
**B:** Of course. It will help reduce your pain and let you sleep better.

A. why do I need this medicine
B. what this medicine is for
C. what is this medicine for

**20. A:** My son is sick. I wonder _______ to children as well as to adults.
**B:** I think they do, but you should call to make sure.

A. is treatment offered at the health clinic
B. does the health clinic offer treatment
C. if the health clinic offers treatment

NAME______________________

# READING I

**Read the next page and answer these questions. What is the correct answer: A, B, C, or D?**

**21.** What is the main purpose of this article?

A. to explain what to do if you can't stop someone's bleeding

B. to explain some basic types of first aid

C. to explain what to do if someone is bleeding badly

D. to explain how to use pressure points to stop bleeding

**22.** According to the article, why should you *not* remove the cloth that is directly on top of the injury?

A. Removing it could cause the bleeding to increase.

B. Removing it could increase the chance of infection.

C. Removing it could cause the person pain.

D. Removing it could cause the person to go into shock.

**23.** According to the article, which of the following should you do first for a person who's bleeding severely?

A. Elevate the injured area.

B. Apply pressure to a pressure point.

C. Call 911.

D. Cover and press on the injury.

**24.** When should you stop applying pressure to a bleeding injury?

A. when you've applied pressure for five minutes

B. when the bleeding stops

C. when you begin to give first aid

D. when blood soaks through the cloth

**25.** Read the article again. What inference can you make?

A. Injuries are usually closer to the heart than to major pressure points.

B. If a person is bleeding badly, he or she will probably become unconscious.

C. It's better to use plastic wrap than cloth to cover an injury.

D. It's harder for blood to reach a part of the body if that part is elevated.

# First Aid for Severe Bleeding

If someone is bleeding badly, you must act quickly. If the person is unconscious, appears to have gone into shock, or is bleeding very severely, call 911 immediately or have someone else call while you begin first aid.

Then, if possible, elevate the injured area above the person's heart in order to reduce blood flow to the injury and slow the bleeding. Next, cover the injury with a clean cloth, towel, or piece of clothing, and use your hand to apply firm pressure. As the blood flow slows down, it will become easier to stop the bleeding with pressure. If blood soaks through the cloth, do not remove it because this could reopen the injury and make the bleeding worse. Just add another cloth on top. Keep pressure on the injury until the bleeding stops. Once it does stop, tightly wrap another cloth, plastic wrap, or tape around the cloth to keep it in place while you wait for help to arrive.

If you are unable to stop the bleeding by elevating the injury and applying pressure to it, then apply pressure to the nearest major pressure point. These points can be found on the inside of the upper arm between the shoulder and elbow and in the area where the leg joins the body. At these points, blood vessels are near the surface of the skin. Pressing on these blood vessels will slow the blood flow even more. Press on the point between the heart and the injury and continue to apply pressure until help arrives.

# READING II

**Read the next page and answer these questions. What is the correct answer: A, B, C, or D?**

**26.** What is the main idea of the article?

A. Take responsibility for your health by asking questions about your health care provider's advice and instructions.

B. Take responsibility for your health by getting health insurance or finding a good clinic.

C. Take responsibility for your health by establishing a relationship with a health care provider and getting regular checkups and preventive health care.

D. Take responsibility for your health by getting immunizations and taking medication.

**27.** What is a possible result of not treating certain medical conditions?

A. serious health problems

B. necessary immunizations

C. expensive health insurance

D. regular preventive health care

**28.** Which of the following is true about health clinics?

A. They are all free.

B. You can't make appointments.

C. They often provide low-cost health care.

D. You need health insurance to go to a clinic.

**29.** Which of the following does the article *not* recommend?

A. telling your doctor about all of your symptoms

B. getting regular checkups

C. talking honestly with your health care provider

D. making an appointment whenever you have a question about your health

30. Read the article again. What inference can you make?

A. You should call your doctor regularly, even if your health has not changed.

B. It's recommended to get a checkup two times a year.

C. You can receive preventive care at health clinics.

D. You should look for a doctor who is a specialist in your health condition.

# Take Responsibility for Your Health

Regular checkups, preventive health screenings, and immunizations are among the most important ways to ensure your good health. Left untreated, many medical conditions may worsen and lead to serious health problems. So it's important to receive regular preventive health care. If you don't have a doctor or other health care provider, then your first step in taking responsibility for your health is to find one. Although health care can be expensive, you may be able to find some cheaper options, even if you have little or no health insurance. For example, clinics offer health care at low or no cost to patients. To find a clinic in your area, you can use the Yellow Pages (look under *clinics*) or visit the U.S. Department of Health and Human Services' website at http://ask.hrsa.gov/pc. Type in your address to get a list of health care centers that provide low-cost or free health care.

Once you find a doctor's office or clinic, make an appointment. Even if you're not sick, you should have a check-up every few years (or more often). Establish a relationship with your health care provider. This means working together with your doctor or nurse in all aspects of your health. Answer all questions honestly and completely. Talk to your doctor or nurse about any questions or concerns you may have about your health, even if they're embarrassing. Mention any symptoms you've been experiencing, even if they seem unimportant. Then your doctor or nurse can recommend which health screenings and immunizations you might need. Make sure you understand your health care provider's advice and instructions before you leave the doctor's office or clinic.

Maintain the relationship with your health care provider even between appointments. If any aspect of your health changes or if you have any questions or concerns, call your doctor's office or clinic for advice. Take an active role in your health. You deserve it!

# WRITING

## Read the next page and answer these questions. What is the correct answer: A, B, C, or D?

**31.** What is the writer's reason for writing this essay?

A. to get readers to agree with his or her point of view

B. to provide readers with background information about the topic

C. to inform readers about the topic

D. to explain how people's points of view have been changing

**32.** Which of the following is an example that supports the third reason in the chart?

A. Nonsmokers often feel that their coworkers who smoke take longer and more frequent breaks than those who don't smoke. This can cause resentment among nonsmoking workers and can affect their work.

B. Nonsmokers shouldn't have to pay as much for health insurance as smokers. Smokers' health costs are higher, so they should have to pay more.

C. Companies should offer free programs to help smokers quit smoking if they want to. The programs would initially cost the companies money, but they'd save money in the long run with lower healthcare costs.

D. Smokers are more likely to have children who smoke. The pattern can carry on for generations.

**33.** Read the beginning of the writer's introductory paragraph for the essay. Which sentence best completes the paragraph by stating the main idea?

A. I think nonsmoking hiring policies are good because employees who smoke cost their employers money in several different ways.

B. In my opinion, smokers should have to pay more for health insurance than nonsmokers because smokers' health costs are higher.

C. I believe that smokers and nonsmokers should have equal job opportunities.

D. I agree with companies' policies to prohibit smoking in the workplace because it can reduce the health care costs of both smoking and nonsmoking employees.

# Outline of Essay

ARGUMENT: Companies shouldn't hire smokers.

**Reason 1:**
The costs of smokers' health care are big expenses for companies.

**Details/Examples:**
Because of diseases related to smoking, health care costs for smokers can be up to 40 percent higher than those for nonsmokers.

**Reason 2:**
Companies suffer from indirect costs of smoking.

**Details/Examples:**
Smokers' yearly productivity rates are often lower than those of nonsmokers due to missed work. Smokers take an average of 14 more sick days per year than nonsmokers.

**Reason 3:**
Smoking in the workplace can affect the work of nonsmokers.

**Details/Examples:**
______________________________
______________________________
______________________________
32.

Most employers in the U.S. have adopted nonsmoking polices for the workplace. And in recent years another trend has developed among employers: They're not hiring smokers. __________
33.

NAME ____________________

# Unit 7 Test

## LISTENING I

***(Tracks 51–54)*** **You will hear a question. Then you will hear a conversation. After that, you will hear the question again and three choices. What is the correct answer: A, B, or C?**

**1.** A. U.S. citizens
B. non-citizens, residents, and visitors
C. U.S. citizens, non-citizens, residents, and visitors

**2.** A. The English arrived.
B. The French arrived.
C. The Spanish arrived.

**3.** A. She's going to become a citizen.
B. She's going to vote.
C. She's not going to vote.

**4.** A. Virginia
B. Massachusetts
C. England

## LISTENING II

***(Tracks 55–58)*** **You will hear a conversation. Then you will hear three sentences. Which sentence is true: A, B, or C?**

**5.** A. The bill passed the House.
B. The President signed the bill.
C. The bill goes to the Senate next.

**6.** A. The man can apply for citizenship now.
B. The man doesn't have an I-551 card.
C. The man is a permanent resident.

**7.** A. Joan Nelson was elected.
B. The Senate elected Joan Nelson.
C. Joan Nelson passed an important bill.

**8.** A. The man's family members are U.S. citizens.
B. The man wants to become a citizen.
C. The man is a citizen.

NAME ______________________________

## LIFE SKILLS

**Read the next page and answer these questions. What is the correct answer: A, B, C, or D?**

**9.** Which of the following is *not* part of this map?

A. a map scale

B. a compass rose

C. a map key

D. a road map

**10.** What does the —— • • —— line indicate?

A. a river

B. a border between states

C. a border between countries

D. an ocean

**11.** Which body of water is east of the United States?

A. the Atlantic Ocean

B. the Gulf of Mexico

C. the Pacific Ocean

D. Lake Superior

**12.** How many states share a border with the state of Iowa?

A. four

B. five

C. six

D. seven

**13.** What is the capital of the state of Michigan?

A. Wisconsin

B. Ohio

C. Lake Michigan

D. Lansing

nationalatlas.gov™
Where We Are
STATES AND CAPITALS
state border
international border
state capital
CANADA
MEXICO
PACIFIC OCEAN
ATLANTIC OCEAN
GULF OF MEXICO
THE BAHAMAS
CUBA
WASHINGTON
Olympia
OREGON
Salem
CALIFORNIA
Sacramento
NEVADA
Carson City
IDAHO
Boise
MONTANA
Helena
WYOMING
Cheyenne
UTAH
Salt Lake City
ARIZONA
Phoenix
COLORADO
Denver
NEW MEXICO
Santa Fe
NORTH DAKOTA
Bismarck
SOUTH DAKOTA
Pierre
NEBRASKA
Lincoln
KANSAS
Topeka
OKLAHOMA
Oklahoma City
TEXAS
Austin
MINNESOTA
St Paul
IOWA
Des Moines
MISSOURI
Jefferson City
ARKANSAS
Little Rock
LOUISIANA
Baton Rouge
WISCONSIN
Madison
ILLINOIS
Springfield
MISSISSIPPI
Jackson
MICHIGAN
Lansing
Lake Superior
Lake Michigan
Lake Huron
INDIANA
Indianapolis
KENTUCKY
Frankfort
TENNESSEE
Nashville
ALABAMA
Montgomery
OHIO
Columbus
WEST VIRGINIA
Charleston
GEORGIA
Atlanta
FLORIDA
Tallahassee
SOUTH CAROLINA
Columbia
NORTH CAROLINA
Raleigh
VIRGINIA
Richmond
PENNSYLVANIA
Harrisburg
NEW YORK
Albany
MAINE
Augusta
VERMONT
Montpelier
NEW HAMPSHIRE
Concord
MASSACHUSETTS
Boston
RHODE ISLAND
Providence
CONNECTICUT
Hartford
NEW JERSEY
Trenton
DELAWARE
Dover
MARYLAND
Annapolis
DC
Washington
N
S
E
W
0 100 200 300 mi
0 100 200 300 km
ALASKA
Juneau
ARCTIC OCEAN
GULF OF ALASKA
BERING SEA
0 200 mi
0 200 km
HAWAII
Honolulu
0 100 mi
0 100 km
U.S. Department of the Interior
U.S. Geological Survey
The National Atlas of the United States of America®

NAME ______________________

# GRAMMAR

## Complete each conversation. What is the correct answer: A, B, or C?

**14. A:** Sandra's husband is American, and she became a U.S. citizen when she married him.

**B:** No, that's not right. She ______ a citizen before she met her husband.

A. wasn't
B. had already become
C. hadn't been

**15. A:** Who arrived in North America first: the settlers at Jamestown or the Pilgrims?

**B:** The settlers at Jamestown. By the time the Pilgrims arrived, the settlers in Jamestown ______ here for 13 years.

A. were
B. hadn't been yet
C. had been

**16. A:** I hear that Senator Byrnes strongly supports Senator Johnson's plan for healthcare reform.

**B:** That's right. She's supported the plan ever since it ______.

A. got introduced
B. introduced
C. had introduced

**17. A:** What's going on with the energy bill? Do you know?

**B:** Yes, it ______ in the Senate last night, so now it goes to the House of Representatives.

A. had approved
B. approved
C. got approved

**18. A:** Did you know that Paul Revere is an American hero today because of the poem "Paul Revere's Ride"? When he died, most people ______ about his ride for freedom. The poem made him famous again.

**B:** That's interesting. I never knew that.

A. got forgotten
B. had forgotten
C. didn't forget

**19. A:** Is the House of Representatives going to vote on that bill?

**B:** No, unfortunately not. The bill ______ when it was reviewed by the committee.

A. had rejected
B. rejected
C. got rejected

**20. A:** Why do Americans celebrate Independence Day on July 4?

**B:** Because it was on that day in 1776 that representatives of the 13 colonies ______ the Declaration of Independence.

A. signed
B. had signed
C. got signed

NAME ______________________

# READING I

## Read the next page and answer these questions. What is the correct answer: A, B, C, or D?

**21.** What is the main idea of this reading?

A. The U.S. Constitution is a very important document that explains the organization of our federal government and the president's duties.

B. The U.S. Constitution created three branches of government, designed to balance each other so that no single branch could have too much control.

C. In the U.S. Constitution, the Founding Fathers organized the government so that the executive branch would lead the other two.

D. The U.S. Constitution explains that Congress is the legislative branch, which is made up of the members of the Senate and the House of Representatives.

**22.** What are the main points covered in the reading?

A. the Founding Fathers, Congress, and the president

B. 1789, veto power, and the Supreme Court

C. checks and balances and the three branches of government

D. the U.S. Constitution, Congress, and the Supreme Court

**23.** How can the president balance the power of Congress?

A. The president can override a veto.

B. The president can pass a new bill.

C. The president can override Congress's vote.

D. The president can veto a bill.

**24.** How can the legislative branch balance the power of the executive branch?

A. It can decide that a president's veto doesn't agree with the Constitution.

B. It controls how money is spent.

C. It enforces the laws passed by the president.

D. It can veto the president's bills.

**25.** Read the article again. What inference can you make?

A. If a bill doesn't receive a two-thirds vote by Congress after a veto, it doesn't become a law.

B. If the Supreme Court decides that a law agrees with the Constitution, it can veto the law.

C. If the president agrees with Congress, he or she becomes the head of the legislative branch.

D. A two-thirds vote by the Supreme Court justices is required to decide that a law doesn't agree with the Constitution.

## Checks and Balances in the U.S. Federal Government

Written in 1789 by the Founding Fathers, the U.S. Constitution provides the organizing principles for our federal government. The Constitution describes the three branches, or parts, of this government: the legislative branch, the executive branch, and the judicial branch. It also explains how these three branches of government work with each other. A system called checks and balances keeps a balance of power among the branches and makes sure that no branch has too much control.

- The legislative branch, also called Congress, is made up of two houses—the Senate and the House of Representatives. Members of Congress are elected by the people of each state and are responsible for making the laws of the country. Congress writes bills and then votes on them. After Congress approves a bill, it then goes to the president (who is part of the executive branch). If the president signs the bill, it becomes a law. If the president wants to stop a bill, he can veto it. In most cases, this will prevent the bill from becoming law. However, Congress can override the president's veto with a new vote, provided that two-thirds (2/3) of all members of Congress vote in favor of the bill. In this way the president (or executive branch) can check the power of Congress with a veto, but Congress can also check the power of the president by overriding the veto. This system allows the president and Congress to balance each other's power.

- The executive branch is headed by the president. He or she signs bills into laws or vetoes them. The president also enforces the government's laws, but he or she needs money to do this. Only Congress can provide the money. Here, Congress (the legislative branch) checks the executive branch through the power to control how money is spent.

- The judicial branch is made up of the Supreme Court and the lower federal courts. The nine justices, or judges, on the Supreme Court decide if laws agree with the Constitution. The Supreme Court can check the other branches of government if it decides a law doesn't agree with the Constitution.

# READING II

## Read the next page and answer these questions. What is the correct answer: A, B, C, or D?

**26.** What is the purpose of this information?

A. It explains some of the questions on the U.S. naturalization test.

B. It provides information about the requirements for applying for citizenship.

C. It explains some of the rights and responsibilities of naturalized U.S. citizens.

D. It provides instructions on how to file an application for naturalization.

**27.** Which of the following is *not* identified as a general requirement for naturalization?

A. residence and physical presence in the U.S.

B. attachment to the Constitution

C. exceptions and other requirements for naturalization

D. knowledge of U.S. history and government

**28.** Six years ago, Angelo became a legal permanent resident of the U.S. The next year he returned to his country for thirteen months. Now he's living in the U.S. again. Does he meet the residency and physical presence requirements for naturalization?

A. Yes, he meets all the residency and physical presence requirements.

B. No, he doesn't, because he hasn't lived in the U.S. for 30 months.

C. No, he doesn't, because he hasn't been a legal permanent resident for long enough.

D. No, he doesn't, because he left the U.S. for longer than a year during the past five years.

**29.** Which of the following is true?

A. Applicants must read the U.S. Constitution before they become citizens.

B. Applicants must take a course in U.S. history and government before they apply for citizenship.

C. Applicants must show proof of taking an approved English course before they apply for citizenship.

D. Applicants must fulfill all other requirements before they take the oath of allegiance.

**30.** Read the information again. What inference can you make?

A. You probably don't have to show your I-551 card as part of the application.

B. If you have a background of violent crimes, you probably won't be considered to have good moral character.

C. Leaving the U.S., even if it is for a short period of time, does not show good moral character.

D. Any foreign citizen who has lived in the U.S. for at least five years can become a U.S. citizen.

# The Path to Citizenship

Naturalization is the process by which foreign citizens obtain U.S. citizenship. The general requirements for naturalization include the following:*

**Age:** Applicants must be 18 years of age or older.

**Residency:** Applicants must have been legal permanent residents of the U.S. for at least five years. Applicants must provide their I-551 card as proof of legal permanent residency.

**Residence and Physical Presence:** Applicants must have lived in the U.S. for at least five years without leaving the country for longer than one year at a time. Applicants must have been physically present in the U.S. for at least 30 months of those 5 years.

**Good Moral Character:** Applicants must demonstrate good moral character, meaning that they contribute to the order and well-being of the U.S. Good moral character is usually determined by confirming that an applicant does not have a background of certain types of crimes, such as violent crimes or crimes against the government.

**Attachment to the Constitution:** Applicants must show that they agree with the principles of the U.S. Constitution.

**Language:** Applicants must be able to read, write, speak, and understand basic English.

**U.S. History and Government Knowledge:** Applicants must demonstrate a basic knowledge of the history of the U.S. and an understanding of the fundamentals of its government.

**Oath of Allegiance:** The last step in the path to citizenship is taking the oath of allegiance. In taking this oath, applicants promise to give up loyalty to all other countries, to support the U.S. Constitution, and to perform military or non-military duties in the U.S. Armed Forces if called.

*These are general requirements. Some exceptions, as well as further restrictions, may apply.

## WRITING

**Read the next page and answer these questions. What is the correct answer: A, B, C, or D?**

**31.** How did the writer structure the first paragraph of her e-mail?

A. She presented the problem and then explained why it is a problem.

B. She presented the problem and examples of the problem.

C. She presented a goal and the problem with reaching that goal.

D. She presented the problem and a possible solution.

**32.** How did the writer structure the second paragraph of her e-mail?

A. She presented a problem and its possible solution.

B. She offered a solution and examples of the solution.

C. She offered a solution and an explanation of why that solution would work.

D. She offered several solutions to the problem.

**33.** Which of the following would be the best way to end this e-mail?

A. Thank you for reading my e-mail. I hope you now understand why the lack of funding for adult ESOL programs is such a problem.

B. Thank you for your time. I look forward to your response.

C. Thank you. Because you are my representative, it's your responsibility to fix this problem.

D. Thank you for your help. This problem has continued to grow for several years.

**From:** Carmen Diaz <cdiaz@coldmail.com>
**Date:** Wed, 10 Oct 2010 11:43:14
**To:** Representative Carlos Lopez-Cantera <carlos.lopez-cantera@myfloridahouse.gov>
**Subject:** Funding for adult ESOL classes

Dear Representative Lopez-Cantera,

I am writing to express my concern about the closing of many of our city's adult ESOL (English for Speakers of Other Languages) programs. For the past several years, funding for these programs has decreased, and fewer and fewer classes are being offered. The result is that there aren't enough classes available to teach all the students who want to learn English. Many employers require workers to read, write, and speak English well. In order to be successful workers, our residents must learn good English language skills. The lack of funding for their learning is a serious problem.

As a solution to the problem, I urge you to increase the city budget for adult ESOL classes. Giving financial priority to adult language learning will help our city's residents improve their English skills so they can get and keep jobs that pay well. With strong English skills, residents can get even better jobs and can perhaps take advantage of opportunities for further education. This would lead to a stronger economy. If you work to increase the city budget for adult ESOL programs, you will help both our residents and our economy.

______________
33.

Sincerely,
Carmen Díaz

NAME________________________________

# Unit 8 Test

## LISTENING I

***(Tracks 59–62)* You will hear a question. Then you will hear a conversation. After that, you will hear the question again and three choices. What is the correct answer: A, B, or C?**

**1.** A. She got stopped by the police tonight.
B. She had to go to traffic school.
C. She's gotten two tickets.

**2.** A. his right to stop answering questions
B. his right to talk to an attorney
C. his right to be his own attorney

**3.** A. The case is being investigated.
B. The parents are in jail.
C. The children are in foster care.

**4.** A. pay the fine
B. request a trial
C. fight the ticket in court

## LISTENING II

***(Tracks 63–66)* You will hear a conversation. Then you will hear three sentences. Which sentence is true: A, B, or C?**

**5.** A. Jeff is going to vote today.
B. Jeff isn't going to vote in the next election.
C. Jeff isn't able to vote.

**6.** A. The woman is a victim of sexual harassment.
B. The woman's boss gave the woman a bad evaluation.
C. The woman welcomes her boss's behavior.

**7.** A. There will be a big penalty.
B. The son has to do community service.
C. The crime is a misdemeanor.

**8.** A. The woman hasn't received any overdue notices.
B. The woman has an overdue library book.
C. The woman got a citation.

NAME________________________________

# LIFE SKILLS

## Read the next page and answer these questions. What is the correct answer: A, B, C, or D?

**9.** Who does Title IX of the Education Amendments of 1972 protect?

A. students

B. students and teachers

C. students and all school employees

D. teachers, other school employees, and non-employees

**10.** Which of the following topics is *not* addressed in the article?

A. examples of sexual harassment

B. ages of possible sexual harassment victims

C. results of sexual harassment

D. sexual harassment of teachers

**11.** According to the article, which of the following is true?

A. The punishment for first-time offenders is less harsh than that for people who have already committed sexual harassment.

B. Females are more frequently victims of sexual harassment than males.

C. Sexual harassment may cause a student's grades to fall.

D. Sexual harassment happens more often at school activities than in the classroom.

**12.** Read the article again. What inference can you make?

A. Most sexual harassment of students comes from other students.

B. Someone who sexually harasses one person may also sexually harass others.

C. Sexual harassment is more common in secondary schools than in colleges.

D. If a student has difficulty learning, the cause is probably sexual harassment.

**13.** Read the paragraph. According to the article, is Danny guilty of sexual harassment?

Sarah and Danny go to school together. Danny asked Sarah out and she agreed. On the date, though, Danny told a lot of jokes of a sexual nature that weren't funny. After that date, Sarah told Danny she didn't want to go out with him again. She's been trying to avoid him at school, but he keeps asking when they're going to go out again. Now he's sending her e-mails and text messages with sexual content, too. Danny's behavior is really bothering Sarah, and she's having trouble concentrating in her classes.

A. Yes, because they attend the same school.

B. No, because they weren't at school when they went on the date.

C. Yes, because his actions are unwelcome.

D. No, because his offer to go on a date was welcome.

# Sexual Harassment at School

Many people know that there are laws in place to offer employees protection from sexual harassment in the workplace, but some people may not know that students are also protected by sexual harassment laws. Title IX of the Education Amendments of 1972 prohibits sexual harassment of students in education programs and activities that receive federal financial assistance from the U.S. Department of Education. (This includes public school systems.) The law applies to every student at every level of education, whether the harassment comes from a school employee, another student, or a nonemployee involved in a school activity, such as a visiting speaker.

Sexual harassment is unwelcome verbal, nonverbal, or physical conduct that is sexual in nature and may make it difficult or impossible for a student to learn. The conduct can negatively affect a student's performance in school and/or participation in school activities. Some examples of sexual harassment include, but are not limited to, the following:

- making sexual propositions or pressuring students for sexual favors
- inappropriate touching and gestures
- displaying or distributing drawings, pictures, written materials, or e-mails with sexual content.
- telling jokes of a sexual nature.

Sexual harassment can be a problem at all ages and at all educational levels, including elementary and secondary schools, as well as at colleges and adult schools. It can affect any student, male or female.

If you or any student you know are a victim of sexual harassment, you should immediately tell a teacher, counselor, principal, or other trusted school employee. Ignoring the situation will not make it go away. Speaking up is the only way to stop the harassment and perhaps even to protect others from being victims.

# GRAMMAR

## Complete each conversation. What is the correct answer: A, B, or C?

**14. A:** What happens if you refuse to take a blood alcohol concentration test?

**B:** Well, it depends on the state. If you refuse in this state, ________ a fine. The officer can also suspend your driver's license.

A. you'll have to pay
B. if you have to pay
C. will have to pay

**15. A:** Do you remember how I got a parking ticket a few weeks ago? Well, now I can't find the ticket. Do you think I still have to pay it?

**B:** Yes! You'd better find it and pay it soon. If you don't pay it on time, ________ a late fee, plus the cost of the ticket.

A. you could charge
B. you couldn't be charged
C. you'll be charged

**16. A:** What's the difference between an infraction and a misdemeanor?

**B:** An infraction is a less serious offense. Depending on the crime, you might go to jail for up to a year for a misdemeanor. But you'll probably just have to pay a fine ________ an infraction.

A. if you commit
B. if you'll commit
C. if you could commit

**17. A:** It's already 8:00, and we were supposed to be there at 7:30.

**B:** I know, but you're driving too fast. If you don't slow down, ________.

A. you get a speeding ticket
B. whether you'll get a speeding ticket
C. you'll get a speeding ticket

**18. A:** They're expecting a lot of people to vote in tomorrow's election.

**B:** I know. If you ________, you'll have to go early.

A. won't want to wait in line
B. don't want to wait in line
C. may not want to wait in line

**19. A:** Does a person go to jail for shoplifting in this state?

**B:** I think it depends on the person's record. If ________ the first time the person has been in trouble, he or she probably won't be sent to jail.

A. it'll be
B. it's
C. it might be

**20. A:** My son's school has a "zero-tolerance" drug policy. Does that mean that students will be expelled for any kind of drug possession or use?

**B:** Exactly. If a student is caught possessing or using drugs at school, he or she ________ to leave the school permanently, even if it's the first time the student has been in trouble.

A. will be forced
B. be forced
C. can still force

NAME________________________________

# READING I

**Read the next page and answer these questions. What is the correct answer: A, B, C, or D?**

**21.** What is the main idea of the first paragraph?

A. Although many people were not originally allowed to vote in the U.S., several laws and amendments have expanded the right to nearly all citizens.

B. Although voting is important for U.S. citizens today, some people choose not to exercise their right to vote.

C. Although voting is an important right of U.S. citizens today, all citizens did not use to have the right to vote.

D. Although almost all U.S. citizens now have the right to vote, there is an age requirement.

**22.** What was one result of the Fifteenth Amendment?

A. Voting restrictions such as religion and land ownership were lifted.

B. States could set their own laws for who was allowed to vote.

C. All African Americans were granted the right to vote.

D. States weren't allowed to prohibit African-American men from voting.

**23.** Which of the following sentences from the article expresses an opinion?

A. In fact, voting is probably the most important right Americans have.

B. However, this was not always the case.

C. Little by little, many states lifted some of these restrictions, and more and more white men were allowed to vote.

D. The right to vote was further extended nationally in 1964 with the Twenty-Fifth Amendment and in 1971 with the Twenty-Sixth Amendment.

**24.** Make an inference. What was one way that some states stopped African Americans from voting?

A. Federal examiners in some states stopped African Americans at the polling places.

B. Some states charged a poll tax, which many African Americans couldn't pay.

C. Some states passed the Voting Rights Acts, which required federal examiners to go to polling places.

D. Some states made discrimination, such as passing a literacy test, illegal.

**25.** Read the article again. What other inference can you make?

A. Religion and land ownership were the only original voting restrictions in the U.S.

B. Women officially got the right to vote before African-American men did.

C. Before the Fifteenth Amendment was passed, each state set its own rules about who was allowed to vote.

D. Because of the Twenty-Sixth Amendment, a larger number of young people vote than old people today.

# ★ ★ ★ ★ ★ ★ The Right to Vote ★ ★ ★ ★ ★ ★

It is the right to vote that defines our nation as a democracy. In fact, voting is probably the most important right Americans have. In the U.S. today, all citizens aged 18 or older (with few exceptions) are guaranteed the right to vote. However, this was not always the case. In the nation's earliest history, voting was limited to white males who owned land. Some states also imposed further limitations, such as religious restrictions.

Little by little, many states lifted some of these restrictions, and more and more white men were allowed to vote. But it wasn't until 1870, when the Fifteenth Amendment was added to the Constitution, that the federal government first set national standards for voting. The amendment made it illegal for states to deny the right to vote to any man based on race or color.

This was an important step, but the struggle for African Americans was not over. Some states, especially in the South, introduced restrictions that specifically targeted African-American voters. At a time when much of the African-American population was poor and illiterate, these states required voters to pay a fee, or poll tax, or to pass a literacy test before voting. This inequality wasn't addressed nationally until 1965. The Voting Rights Act passed in that year finally made literacy tests illegal. It also allowed federal examiners to go to polling places to make sure that the law was enforced.

Although all male citizens were granted the right to vote in 1870, women weren't guaranteed that right until 50 years later. In 1920, the Nineteenth Amendment to the Constitution was added. This amendment made it illegal for states to deny any person the right to vote based on sex.

The right to vote was further extended nationally in 1964 with the Twenty-Fifth Amendment and in 1971 with the Twenty-Sixth Amendment. The Twenty-Fifth Amendment made it illegal to charge poll taxes to voters. The Twenty-Sixth Amendment changed the legal voting age across the country from 21 to 18.

NAME ____________________

# READING II

**Read the next page and answer these questions. What is the correct answer: A, B, C, or D?**

**26.** What is the purpose of this article?

A. to explain why employers used to prefer to hire children over adults

B. to provide the history of American child labor laws

C. to provide information about child labor laws in the U.S.

D. to compare federal child labor laws with similar state laws

**27.** Which of the following FLSA protections does the article *not* mention?

A. minimum ages for children working on farms

B. weekly maximums for the number of hours a child can work

C. minimum hourly pay for all workers

D. the opportunity for young workers to go to school

**28.** Which of the following sentences from the article expresses an opinion?

A. Children could work in smaller spaces and use some machines faster than adult workers could.

B. This was probably one of the most important steps to ensuring the well-being of American children.

C. The FLSA has been updated several times since 1938 to further protect the health, safety, and educational opportunities of children.

D. When federal and state standards differ, the rules that provide the most protection to young workers apply.

**29.** Salim is 15 years old, and he works part-time at a grocery store after school and on weekends. Which of the following schedules is he *not* allowed to work?

A. Monday 3:00 P.M.–6:00 P.M., Wednesday 3:00 P.M.–6:00 P.M., Friday 4:00 P.M.–7:00 P.M.

B. Tuesday 4:00 P.M.–7:00 P.M., Thursday 4:00 P.M.–7:00 P.M., Saturday 11:00 A.M.–7:00 P.M.

C. Tuesday 4:00 P.M.–7:00 P.M., Thursday 4:00 P.M.–7:00 P.M., Saturday 11:00 A.M.–6:00 P.M., Sunday 11:00 A.M.–3:00 P.M.

D. Friday 4:00 P.M.–9:00 P.M., Saturday 12:00 P.M.–8:00 P.M., Sunday 12:00 P.M.–8:00 P.M.

**30.** Read the article again. What inference can you make?

A. Some states' laws provide more protection for young workers than the laws of the federal government.

B. Young workers can work fewer hours during the summer months than they can during the school year.

C. According to the FLSA, children must receive a higher hourly pay than adult workers.

D. There are no limitations on the type of work children can do when they're 16 or older.

# Child Labor Laws

In the 1800s and early 1900s, American employers often hired children. Children could work in smaller spaces and work faster on some machines than adult workers could. Employers could pay children less than adults. It was not uncommon for children as young as ten to work twelve-hour days, six days a week, doing unhealthy or dangerous work for pennies a day.

But in 1938, President Franklin D. Roosevelt signed into law the Fair Labor Standards Act (FLSA). This was probably one of the most important steps to ensuring the well-being of American children. Among other things, the act restricted the number of hours and types of work children could do, and it ensured them a minimum hourly pay rate.

The FLSA has been updated several times since 1938 to further protect the health, safety, and educational opportunities of children. The law sets restrictions on workers under the age of 18, with some stricter rules for those under the age of 16. The FLSA sets 14 as the minimum age for most non-agricultural work. Here are some examples of the kinds of rules established by the FLSA for young workers:

- Workers under the age of 18 are not permitted to work in any job that is classified as hazardous, including manufacturing explosives, mining, and operating many types of power-driven equipment.
- Workers of all ages must be paid at least the federal hourly minimum wage.
- Workers who are 14 to 15 years of age and employed in non-farm employment are *not* permitted to work
    - during school hours.
    - during the hours of 7 P.M. to 7 A.M. (9 P.M. to 7 A.M. from June 1 through Labor Day).
    - more than 3 hours on a school day and/or more than 18 hours during a school week.
    - more than 8 hours on a non-school day and/or more than 40 hours during a non-school week.

It is important to note that today all states provide their own child labor standards as well. When federal and state standards differ, the rules that provide the most protection to young workers apply.

## WRITING

### Read the next page and answer these questions. What is the correct answer: A, B, C, or D?

**31.** Choose the phrase that correctly signals the sentence that follows it.

A. contrary to the American system

B. like the American system

C. also the American system

D. unlike the American system

**32.** Choose the sentence that is correctly signaled by the phrase *In contrast.*

A. Malaysian citizens have the right to a trial by jury

B. juries in Malaysia decide if a defendant is innocent or guilty

C. the Malaysian legal system does not include the use of juries

D. a jury of seven people listens to and decides each case in Malaysia

**33.** What is the structure of this essay?

A. paragraph 1 = one similarity
paragraph 2 = a second similarity
paragraph 3 = differences

B. paragraph 1 = introduction
paragraph 2 = one similarity and one difference
paragraph 3 = a second similarity and a second difference

C. paragraph 1 = one similarity and one difference
paragraph 2 = a second similarity
paragraph 3 = a second difference

D. paragraph 1 = introduction
paragraph 2 = similarities
paragraph 3 = differences

## The Legal Systems of Malaysia and the United States

The legal system of my home country of Malaysia may seem very different from that of the U.S. However, a closer look at the systems of the two countries reveals some similarities as well as some differences.

Both Malaysia and the U.S. were once British colonies. When they became independent countries, both based much of their legal systems on the British one, which explains some of the systems' similarities. For example, ___________ (31.), Malaysia's legal system is based on common laws, which are laws created by the courts, not the government. Another similarity is that in the U.S. and in Malaysia the legal systems are separate from the executive and legislative branches of government.

The biggest difference between the legal systems of the two nations can be seen in the way trials are conducted. The legal system in the U.S. guarantees anyone accused of a serious crime the right to a trial by jury. The jury, which is made up of 12 people, hears the evidence of the case and determines whether the person is innocent or guilty. In contrast, ___________ (32.). Cases are tried by a judge, who, with the help of two assessors, decides a defendant's innocence or guilt.

NAME ________________

# Unit 9 Test

## LISTENING I

***(Tracks 67–70)* You will hear a question. Then you will hear a conversation. After that, you will hear the question again and three choices. What is the correct answer: A, B, or C?**

**1.** A. trash
B. paper
C. metal, glass, and plastic

**2.** A. replace their lightbulbs more often
B. get the lightbulbs with the lowest price
C. buy energy-efficient lightbulbs

**3.** A. the effects of cutting down trees
B. the effects of carbon dioxide
C. the causes of environmental problems

**4.** A. recycle the boxes
B. reuse the boxes
C. buy some boxes

## LISTENING II

***(Tracks 71–74)* You will hear a conversation. Then you will hear three sentences. Which sentence is true: A, B, or C?**

**5.** A. The man carpools with Alicia.
B. The woman wants to start carpooling.
C. The man suggests a way to save money.

**6.** A. The man didn't recycle on his trip.
B. The woman wants more recycling in her city.
C. The man is going to recycle more plastic.

**7.** A. The man is eating less.
B. The man is spending too much on gas.
C. The man is saving money on gas.

**8.** A. the woman says to give the plants shade
B. the woman suggests watering the plants
C. the woman recommends native plants

## LIFE SKILLS

### Read the next page and answer these questions. What is the correct answer: A, B, C, or D?

**9.** Jamal lives on the East Side. When can he leave his garbage out for collection?

A. Mondays and Thursdays

B. Mondays and Fridays

C. Tuesdays and Thursdays

D. Tuesdays and Fridays

**10.** On which days can paper be recycled?

A. Wednesday, August 11, and Wednesday, August 25

B. every Monday and Thursday

C. every Wednesday

D. Wednesday, August 4, and Wednesday, August 18

**11.** On which days can glass and plastic be recycled?

A. Only glass can be recycled on August 4, and only plastic can be recycled on August 18.

B. They can both be recycled every Wednesday.

C. Only glass can be recycled on August 4 and 11, and only plastic can be recycled on August 18 and 25.

D. They can both be recycled on August 4 and August 18.

**12.** Which of the following items should *not* be put out for recycling?

A. commingled materials

B. letters and other mail

C. plastic caps

D. metal cans

**13.** What should residents do with hazardous waste?

A. drop it off on Saturday, August 14, or Saturday, August 28

B. drop it off on Saturday, August 7

C. recycle it on Wednesday, August 4, and Wednesday, August 18

D. put it out for collection on Saturday, August 7

# August 2010 Trash/Recycling Schedule

| Sunday | Monday | Tuesday | Wednesday | Thursday | Friday | Saturday |
|---|---|---|---|---|---|---|
| 1 | 2<br>GW | 3<br>GE | 4<br>Recycling-**C** | 5<br>GW | 6<br>GE | 7<br>Household Hazardous Waste Drop-off Day |
| 8 | 9<br>GW | 10<br>GE | 11<br>Recycling-**P** | 12<br>GW | 13<br>GE | 14<br>Scrap Tire Drop-off Day |
| 15 | 16<br>GW | 17<br>GE | 18<br>Recycling-**C** | 19<br>GW | 20<br>GE | 21 |
| 22 | 23<br>GW | 24<br>GE | 25<br>Recycling-**P** | 26<br>GW | 27<br>GE | 28<br>Computer and Electronics Recycling Day |
| 29 | 30<br>GW | 31<br>GE | | | | |

GW = Garbage and trash, West Side
GE = Garbage and trash, East Side
**C** = Commingled (mixed)
**P** = Paper

## RECYCLABLE ITEMS

**Paper**

- newspapers
- magazines
- catalogs
- junk mail
- office paper
- phone books
- paper bags
- boxes

**Commingled**

***Metal***

- food and drink cans
- food trays
- clean aluminum foil

***Glass***

- clean brown, green, and clear containers (put caps in trash)

***Plastic***

- clean containers with numbers 1 and 2 (put caps in trash)

NAME ______________________________

# GRAMMAR

## Complete each conversation. What is the correct answer: A, B, or C?

**14. A:** So, how's it working out to carpool with Tony?

**B:** Great! I wish we ________ to work together years ago.

A. had started driving
B. would have started driving
C. might have started

**15. A:** I can't believe how much trash we've thrown away over the years. I mean, we used to throw out everything—even glass and metal.

**B:** I know. At that time we didn't know how much we were hurting the environment. If we ________, we wouldn't have done it.

A. would have known
B. wish we knew
C. had known

**16. A:** What do you think of the new recycling schedule?

**B:** I wish they ________. I can never remember what to put out on which day.

A. wouldn't have changed it
B. hadn't changed it
C. haven't changed it

**17. A:** Oh, you get *Family Time* magazine. I just read this week's issue at the library. It has a lot of good information.

**B:** I didn't know they had that magazine at the library. If I'd known that, I ________ a subscription.

A. hadn't paid for
B. wouldn't have paid for
C. couldn't have paid for

**18. A:** Did you know that plastic doesn't biodegrade? When you throw away a plastic water bottle, it remains in the environment *forever.*

**B:** Forever? Wow. I wish I ________ that a long time ago. I'll be sure to recycle them from now on.

A. would have learned
B. would learn
C. had learned

**19. A:** Do you remember when they first passed all the recycling laws in this city?

**B:** Yeah, at first they were hard to get used to, but now they're just a part of life. Imagine, if they hadn't passed those laws, this ________ a very different city.

A. had become
B. would have become
C. that it had become

**20. A:** Wow, you bought some really great things today.

**B:** I know. If I had bought those things at regular stores, I ________ over a hundred dollars. But I only spent $35 at the secondhand shop!

A. would have spent
B. had spent
C. would spend

# READING I

**Read the next page and answer these questions. What is the correct answer: A, B, C, or D?**

**21.** What is the purpose of this information?

A. to provide ideas for ways to reuse paper

B. to give some tips about ways to save time as you help the environment

C. to share some ways to use less paper and save money

D. to invite people to share ways they have helped the environment

**22.** Which of the following does the writer suggest?

A. rereading your old magazines

B. giving away advertisements and catalogs that you don't want

C. sharing magazines with others

D. printing lists and notes on the computer

**23.** Which of the following is *not* true?

A. Readers of this blog can leave comments about it.

B. The tips in the blog are based on the writer's own experience.

C. This blog includes information from the U.S. Environmental Protection Agency.

D. Gisela Fuentes responded to this blog.

**24.** Look at the blog again. How much of America's trash is paper products?

A. about 50 percent

B. a little more than 30 percent

C. 25 percent

D. less than 15 percent

**25.** Read the article again. What inference can you make?

A. Cloth napkins are more formal and nicer than paper ones.

B. Cloth napkins cost more than paper napkins at first, but they last longer.

C. Cloth napkins won't look as nice after they've been washed hundreds of times.

D. Cloth napkins are more popular than paper napkins.

http://www.giselafuentes.com

# Simple Steps for Saving Paper *and* Money

**July 7, 2010 by Gisela Fuentes**

For the past few months, I've been trying to reduce the amount of paper I use. I found that it's not as hard as I thought, and I'm actually saving money! Here are a few tips that have helped me save paper and money at the same time.

- Stop buying cards and stamps. Send e-cards instead of regular cards. There are lots of websites that offer free e-cards.
- Share magazine subscriptions with a neighbor, friend, or family member. Then, each month you can switch after you've read the magazines you receive. Split the cost, and enjoy twice as many magazines.
- Reduce junk mail. Call or e-mail companies and organizations that send you unwanted materials. Ask them to take you off their mailing lists. Eventually you'll get fewer advertisements, catalogs, and special offers. This won't necessarily save you money, but you'll definitely waste less time looking at mail you don't want.
- Use paper twice. Print on both sides of computer paper. You can also use the backs of the sheets that have already been printed on for writing lists, notes, etc. You can even staple these together to make a "notebook." You'll have to buy paper half as often.
- Instead of buying, using, and throwing away paper napkins, try using cloth ones. You can wash and reuse cloth napkins hundreds of times, which will save you money in the end.
- Here's a chart that I found from the Environmental Protection Agency.

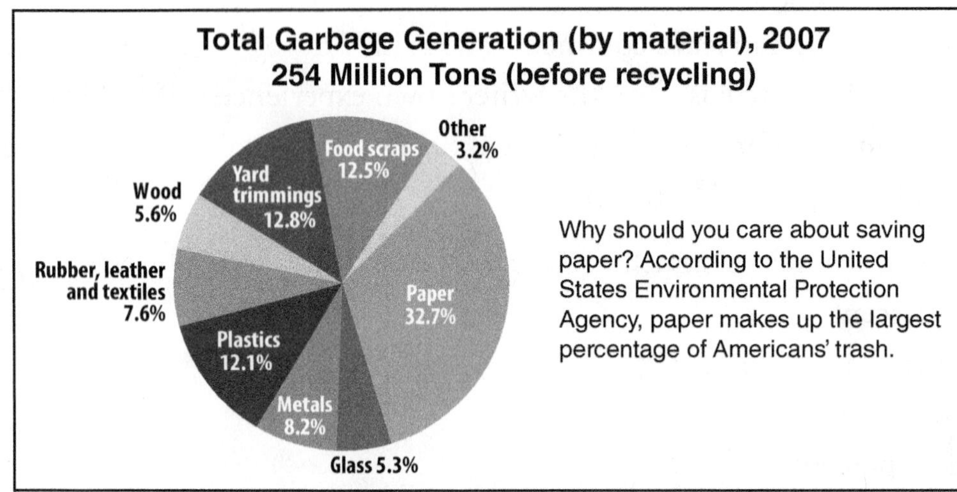


Why should you care about saving paper? According to the United States Environmental Protection Agency, paper makes up the largest percentage of Americans' trash.

**Post your comments**

Name: E-mail:

Location: Message:

## READING II

**Read the next page and answer these questions. What is the correct answer: A, B, C, or D?**

**26.** What is the main idea of this article?

A. American cities should follow Portland's model and try to become more green.

B. Portland's many public parks contribute to its green reputation.

C. Portland is so green because it's located in the northwestern part of the country.

D. Portland is very green because the land has been used well.

**27.** Which of the following details from the reading supports the statement that Portland is a healthy place to live?

A. In the 1970s, most U.S. cities were working to build more roads.

B. Many people walk and ride bikes instead of driving.

C. Forest Park is actually an urban forest.

D. Plans have been made for the areas around the city.

**28.** Which inference can you make based on the information in the article?

A. People have to drive shorter distances to get places, which results in fewer harmful emissions from cars.

B. Because more people walk to work, the city needs more parks and green spaces.

C. Because a lot of food is grown locally, there are more restaurants.

D. Because there are fewer harmful emissions from cars, the city is able to reduce the number of roads needed.

**29.** Which of the following is an example of repurposing?

A. establishing a park where a highway used to be

B. not permitting expansion into the land around a city

C. using roads for both bicycles and cars

D. opening new businesses in a growing city

**30.** Look at the article again. Make an inference. Which statement is probably true?

A. Restaurants in Portland are more expensive than restaurants in other parts of the country.

B. Restaurants don't use the fruits and vegetables that are grown nearby.

C. There are a lot of restaurants in Portland.

D. The restaurants in Portland don't get a lot of business.

# The Greenest City

Located in the northwestern state of Oregon, Portland is often considered to be the "greenest" city in the U.S. Responsible planning and smart land use have helped this city earn its reputation as a healthy, environmentally friendly place to live.

Good urban planning in Portland has resulted in people living, working, and playing within a relatively small area. Shorter distances between destinations means that fewer people use cars. Walking, taking public transportation, and riding bikes are all popular alternatives to driving in this town.

Areas for public parks and green open spaces have been included in Portland's planning. For example, Forest Park, a public park, is actually a forest that grows within the city. It is the largest urban forest—a collection of trees that grow within a city or town—in the U.S.

The city of Portland has been creative in its use of land, including repurposing, or using land in ways that are different from their original purposes. For example, in the 1970s, when the rest of the U.S. was building more and more roads, Portland city planners knocked down a six-lane freeway. In its place, they created a 36-acre park on the edge of the Willamette River.

If you think "green" means fewer businesses, think again. The time and money Portland residents save by driving less translates into more support for local goods and services such as these popular cafés and restaurants—many of which are also green!

But Portland's land use plans aren't limited to urban areas. Tough restrictions have been placed on the nonurban land that surrounds the city. So while many American cities continue to expand into the natural areas around them, Portland's expansion is contained. Much of the land around the city is used for farming, providing the city with a large supply of fresh, local fruit and vegetables.

NAME ______________________________

## WRITING

**Read the next page and answer these questions. What is the correct answer: A, B, C, or D?**

**31.** Choose the phrase that correctly shows the time frame of the sentence that follows.

A. In three months

B. For a long time

C. At that moment

D. As soon as

**32.** Choose the phrase that correctly shows the time frame of the sentences that follow.

A. During that time

B. A month after that

C. Since then

D. Afterward

**33.** Choose the phrase that correctly shows the time frame of the sentences that follow.

A. Finally

B. In the next month

C. Ever since then

D. A few months ago

## New Habits for Our Family

I always knew I should recycle, but I didn't put too much importance on it. Then, three months ago, I saw my daughter throw a metal can into the garbage. ___________ (31.), I realized that I had to set a better example for my kids and teach them the importance of taking care of the environment. So now, each month my kids and I are adding one new earth-friendly habit to our lives.

In the first month, our focus was recycling. ___________ (32.), my kids learned which things could be recycled. We put a container in the kitchen for all the recyclables, and when that got full, we'd sort the items into the correct containers for collection. Now my kids know exactly what can be recycled and which container to put each item in.

___________ (33.), we started to reduce our trash. My kids take their lunches to school now, and I take mine to work. I used to put fruit, cut-up vegetables, and sandwiches into small plastic bags, and then I put those into brown paper bags. And every day at the end of lunch, we threw all the bags away! So at the beginning of our second month, we each picked out a reusable lunch box. I collected some containers. (I didn't even buy them. I just washed and reused things like yogurt and other food containers.) Now I put our food into the containers and the containers in our lunchboxes. Every day we bring the containers and lunchboxes home, wash them, and use them again the next day.

Now we're into our third month. This month we started using cloth bags instead of plastic ones to carry our groceries. So far, this was the hardest thing to get used to. I kept forgetting the bags and leaving them at home until my daughter had the idea to keep the bags in the car. That seems to be working pretty well.

I don't know what our next new habit will be. But I'm really proud of us for working together to make changes that make a difference.

**by Mei Huang**

NAME______________________________

# Unit 10 Test

## LISTENING I

***(Tracks 75–78)* You will hear a question. Then you will hear a conversation. After that, you will hear the question again and three choices. What is the correct answer: A, B, or C?**

**1.** A. using shorthand
B. sending a text
C. spelling correctly

**2.** A. He only sees the pros.
B. He only sees the cons.
C. He sees both pros and cons.

**3.** A. He read a manual and watched videos.
B. He got job training.
C. He played games instead of going to work.

**4.** A. using the same naming system
B. creating a new file
C. switching computers

## LISTENING II

***(Tracks 79–82)* You will hear a conversation. Then you will hear three sentences. Which sentence is true: A, B, or C?**

**5.** A. Harry called on the phone.
B. Harry sent a text message.
C. Harry sent an e-mail.

**6.** A. The man has basic computer skills.
B. The man knows how to create and save documents.
C. The man wants to learn some computer skills.

**7.** A. The man agrees.
B. The man disagrees.
C. The man doesn't have an opinion.

**8.** A. The woman doesn't like to use the Internet.
B. The woman hasn't gotten used to the Internet.
C. The woman's kids taught her to use the Internet.

NAME ____________________

# LIFE SKILLS

## Read the next page and answer these questions. What is the correct answer: A, B, C, or D?

**9.** What does the word *components* refer to in this information?

A. electronic devices that are part of your audio/video system

B. parts of the universal remote

C. other electronic devices' remote controls

D. brand codes

**10.** What do steps 1–6 explain?

A. how to use the Control All to turn on your TV manually

B. how to aim the universal remote at the correct component

C. how to set the universal remote to work with your electronic devices

D. how to find the four-digit code for your electronic devices

**11.** To program the TV, what should you do after the indicator light flashes?

A. hold SET

B. press TV

C. enter the code

D. hit ENTER

**12.** If you want to program the universal remote to control your DVD player, what should you do first?

A. turn on the DVD player

B. aim the universal remote at the DVD player

C. turn off the TV

D. hold SET

**13.** Which number on the diagram shows where to enter the four-digit code?

A. 3

B. 4

C. 5

D. 6

# Control All Universal Remote Owner's Manual

Congratulations on purchasing your Control All universal remote. Replace your other remote controls with this universal remote. Use it to control up to six different components of your home audio/video system, including your TV, DVD, VCR or DVR, cable or satellite, stereo, and auxiliary device.

Program your universal remote to control each component of your audio/video system.

1. Turn on the component you want to program, such as your TV. (Use your old remote or do it manually.)
2. In the chart below, find the four-digit code for the brand of the component you want to program (in this case, your TV).
3. Aim the universal remote at the component you want to program (in this case, your TV set). Press and hold SET until the indicator light starts flashing.
4. Press the button for the component you want to program (in this case, press TV).
5. Enter the four-digit code.
6. Press ENTER.

Repeat these steps for each component you wish to program.

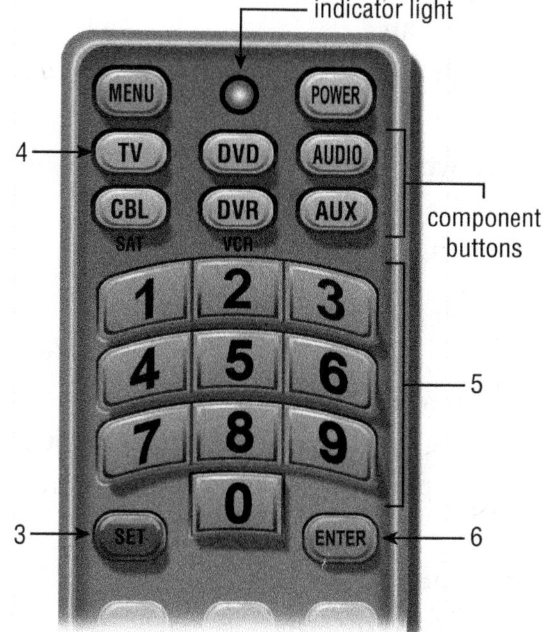


| | TV brand | Code |
|---|---|---|
| 2 | Point | 1412 |
| | Stevens | 1431 |
| | Tamton | 1475 |

| DVD brand | Code |
|---|---|
| Vedia | 2010 |
| PE | 2089 |
| Optic | 2099 |

| Stereo brand | Code |
|---|---|
| Lider | 4326 |
| Tanyo | 4357 |
| Hiro | 4368 |

NAME ____________________

## GRAMMAR

### Complete each conversation. What is the correct answer: A, B, or C?

**14. A:** J. C. R. Licklider is the man ______ that something like the Internet could be created.

**B:** I bet that's an interesting story. I'll have to look him up online.

A. who first had the idea
B. he first had the idea
C. that he first had the idea

**15. A:** I overheard a guy talking in the computer lab today. He said his friend was a "techie." What does that mean?

**B:** A techie is a person ______ a lot about computers and electronic equipment. It's generally a compliment.

A. knows
B. who knows
C. you know

**16. A:** Do you think that the Internet is harming people's communication skills?

**B:** It might be harmful for people ______ it a lot. But in my opinion, the Internet has done more good than harm.

A. that use
B. who use
C. Both A and B are correct.

**17. A:** My son sent me a text message ______. Can you help me?

**B:** Sure. Let's see . . . C-U-L-8-R. Oh, it says "See you later"!

A. that I don't understand
B. I don't understand it
C. who I don't understand

**18. A:** So tell me about the new virtual training at work. It sounds cool.

**B:** It is. There are three different games ______ three different job skills.

A. which practice
B. that practice
C. Both A and B are correct.

**19. A:** What kind of cell phone are you going to get for your daughter?

**B:** I'm not sure. She wants ______ a camera, but I don't think she really needs that.

A. a phone has
B. a phone that has
C. a phone that has it

**20. A:** I want to take a virtual driver's training program. I heard there's a new driving simulator ______ to help you improve your driving skills.

**B:** Hmmm. It sounds interesting—and expensive!

A. who guarantees
B. which guarantees
C. Both A and B are correct.

NAME ____________________

## READING I

**Read the next page and answer these questions. What is the correct answer: A, B, C, or D?**

**21.** What is the purpose of this article?

A. to provide information about virtual job training

B. to warn about the dangers of virtual job training

C. to convince readers that virtual job training is better than other forms of training

D. to entertain readers with a story about how virtual job training has helped some employees

**22.** What is the main idea of the third paragraph?

A. Virtual training video games are more popular than other types of job training.

B. Sometimes employees don't do their work because they're playing virtual training video games.

C. Employees enjoy virtual training video games.

D. Virtual training video games have become more popular in recent years.

**23.** How do workers learn from virtual training?

A. They work closely with other employees.

B. They receive feedback from their employers.

C. They get to practice actual tasks.

D. They are immediately corrected for their mistakes.

**24.** What does the writer of the article predict for the future?

A. Employees will eventually get tired of the games.

B. Employees' productivity will decrease because they will spend too much time playing games.

C. Virtual training won't be effective for many types of jobs.

D. Virtual training technology will change the way workers are trained.

**25.** Read the article again. What inference can you make?

A. Virtual training video games work best for high-level jobs.

B. People learn better when they're motivated.

C. Companies can save a lot of money by using virtual training.

D. Employers enjoy virtual training more than employees do.

# Job Training That's Fun?

When you think of job training, do you imagine fun and games? Probably not, but according to many experts, this is the next big trend in employee training. Welcome to the world of virtual training.

Virtual training uses virtual reality to simulate different learning situations. Basically, a computer creates an environment that seems real to the person who experiences it. Virtual training allows employees to learn by actually doing a task, not just by reading about it in a training manual or watching it on a training video.

One of the most popular forms of virtual training comes in the form of video games. The reason they're popular is that they're fun. Azi Chakwa works on the production line at the Rocky Point ice cream factory where virtual training video games were introduced a few months ago. Chakwa says, "The games are cool. You can really get into them and have a lot of fun. Sometimes you even forget that you're learning." Filomena Nowak works in the company's warehouse. She learned that some of company's virtual training video games can be found on the company website. She says, "The games are so much fun that I even play them on my computer at home!"

So how do employers feel about these fun and games? Carlos Blanco, a supervisor at Rocky Point says, "They're great. Employees are motivated and excited to learn, which has led to positive results. Our employees have really improved their work performance through these training programs."

Virtual training can be used in a variety of different careers. Workers, including computer technicians, customer service representatives, production line workers, and salespeople are all learning through virtual training video games.

Virtual training probably won't ever entirely replace traditional training methods. But it will definitely change the way that many workers are learning.

NAME ____________________

## READING II

**Read the next page and answer these questions. What is the correct answer: A, B, C, or D?**

**26.** What is the purpose of this article?

A. to entertain readers with the story of the Internet's early beginnings

B. to examine the importance of the Internet today

C. to provide information about the history of the Internet

D. to explain why J. C. R. Licklider should be recognized as the inventor of the Internet

**27.** Look at the time line of events from the article. Between which two years should the creation of IPTO be added?

A. between 1957 and 1960

B. between 1960 and 1969

C. between 1971 and 1980

D. between 1980 and 1983

**28.** Why was the IPTO created?

A. to make sure the Soviet Union had a military advantage

B. to create the Internet

C. to further develop computer technology

D. to invent a universal network

**29.** What is the main idea of the last paragraph?

A. Humans should be careful about the Internet in the future.

B. The world has changed a lot since the invention of the Internet.

C. The Internet will continue to have a positive impact on humans' lives.

D. No one is sure what the future of the Internet will be.

**30.** Read the article again. What inference can you make?

A. Without Licklider, the Internet might not exist.

B. At first users were nervous to join the ARPAnet network.

C. The IPTO was disappointed with ARPAnet.

D. The author doesn't believe the Internet will survive in the future.

# The Internet: A Short History

Nowadays, it's hard to imagine the world without the Internet. But the first ideas that led to the Internet's development are less than sixty years old.

The beginnings of the Internet can be traced back to the Advanced Research Project Agency (ARPA), which was created by the U.S. government in 1957 to ensure that the United States would have a military advantage over the Soviet Union. But it soon became clear that no computer programs existed to share and analyze the large amounts of data needed to do the job. So in 1962 the Information Process Techniques Office (IPTO) was created within ARPA for the purpose of researching and making advances in computer technology. J.C.R. Licklider was hired as the IPTO's director. Licklider's idea for a universal network influenced the direction of the IPTO's research, leading it to create the network called ARPAnet in just seven years.

The first exchange of data over the network occurred in 1969 between computers at UCLA and Stanford Research Institute. At first, researchers were able to transmit only two letters before the system failed. But they tried again, and they were successful. Later that year, two more sites were added to the network.

By 1971, nineteen other sites around the country had joined the network. Throughout the 70s, other universities, governmental departments, and researchers continued to join. By the end of the decade, the ARPAnet was so big that its system for communication could no longer support so many users.

For this reason, in 1983, ARPAnet switched to the TCP/IP communication system. From that point, ARPAnet became known as the Internet. The TCP/IP system allowed the number of sites and users to continue to grow faster and faster. This system is still in use today by over one billion users.

It's impossible to know the future of the Internet and the impact it will have on our lives. Some people are optimistic and believe it will help to equalize opportunities among people. Others are afraid that technology is developing faster than humans can adapt to it. One thing is certain: The world will be watching.

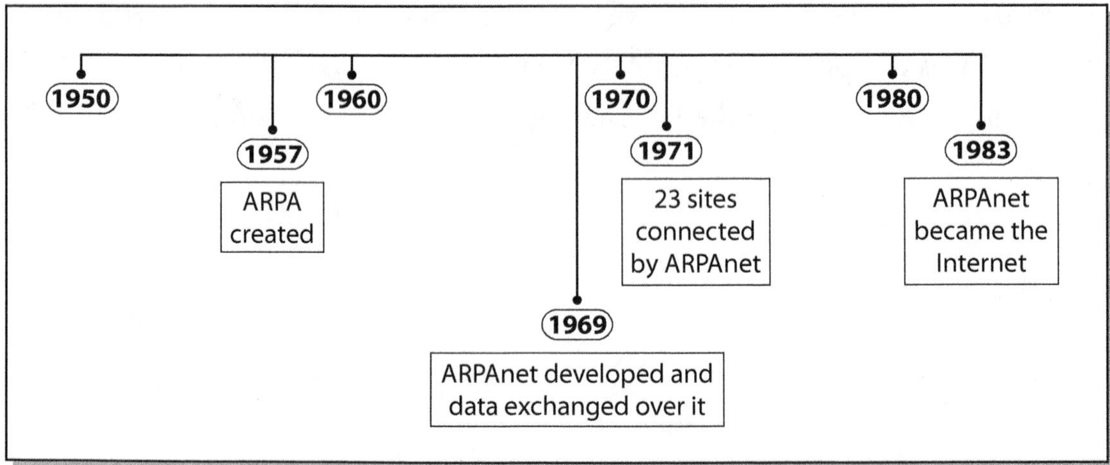

# WRITING

## Read the next page and answer these questions. What is the correct answer: A, B, C, or D?

**31.** Which of the following sentences from the first paragraph uses sensory details to describe the situation?

A. I didn't speak English well, and I was too proud to try.

B. The few times that I did speak English, I got so embarrassed.

C. My face got hot and red, and my mouth went dry.

D. I felt like everyone was laughing at me.

**32.** What details does the writer give about her first day of class?

A. how she felt before and after she met the teacher

B. how she felt at the end of the first class

C. how she felt after making a mistake in class

D. how she felt after trying to talk to her classmates

**33.** Which of the following sentences would add sensory details to the third paragraph?

A. She was a good teacher.

B. She had a soft voice and a warm smile.

C. She had a lot of patience.

D. All the students liked her, especially me.

## A Proud Moment

I moved to the U.S. from Venezuela when I was 18. I didn't speak English well, and I was too proud to try. The few times that I did speak English, I got very embarrassed. My face got hot and red, and my mouth went dry. I felt like everyone was laughing at me.

One night, after I'd been here for a few months, my cousin invited me to dinner with some friends from work. When we arrived, it looked like fun. Everyone was talking and telling stories and laughing. But not one person spoke Spanish, except for my cousin. I couldn't communicate with any of her friends! I was surrounded by people, but I'd never felt so alone in my life. That night I decided that it was time to learn English.

I signed up for classes. On the day of my first class, I felt like a little kid just starting school. I was so nervous! My hands got sweaty, and I felt like I was going to be sick. But the minute my teacher came into the classroom, I felt better. Mrs. Lawson was a sweet, older woman.

I knew that if I could learn from anyone, it would be her. And I did learn! Over the next few months, I studied hard. Slowly, I started to practice speaking English. I tried to talk to some of my classmates. I even signed up for an English conversation group.

Several months later, my cousin invited me to another event with her friends from work. I was nervous, but I went. At first I felt shy. I talked to a few people for a few minutes, but I didn't say much. Then my cousin introduced me to her friend Manny. I said hello, and we started talking. Then some more people came over, and I talked to them, too. Before I knew it, I was having real conversations with people—in English! I made some mistakes—a lot, actually—and I didn't understand everything the first time, but I was really communicating. And it was fun!

That night was important to me. For the first time, I felt really proud of myself for working hard and learning English. To some people, having a few conversations at a party might not seem like a big deal. But to me, I felt like I was finally overcoming a big obstacle. I wasn't done learning yet, but now I had the confidence to keep trying.

by Roxana Treve

# Future 5
# Unit Test Answer Sheet

① ______________________________________________
Last Name First Name Middle

② ______________________________________________
Teacher's Name

TEST

1 (A) (B) (C) (D)
2 (A) (B) (C) (D)
3 (A) (B) (C) (D)
4 (A) (B) (C) (D)
5 (A) (B) (C) (D)
6 (A) (B) (C) (D)
7 (A) (B) (C) (D)
8 (A) (B) (C) (D)
9 (A) (B) (C) (D)
10 (A) (B) (C) (D)
11 (A) (B) (C) (D)
12 (A) (B) (C) (D)
13 (A) (B) (C) (D)
14 (A) (B) (C) (D)
15 (A) (B) (C) (D)
16 (A) (B) (C) (D)
17 (A) (B) (C) (D)
18 (A) (B) (C) (D)
19 (A) (B) (C) (D)
20 (A) (B) (C) (D)
21 (A) (B) (C) (D)
22 (A) (B) (C) (D)
23 (A) (B) (C) (D)
24 (A) (B) (C) (D)
25 (A) (B) (C) (D)
26 (A) (B) (C) (D)
27 (A) (B) (C) (D)
28 (A) (B) (C) (D)
29 (A) (B) (C) (D)
30 (A) (B) (C) (D)
31 (A) (B) (C) (D)
32 (A) (B) (C) (D)
33 (A) (B) (C) (D)

**Directions for marking answers**

- Use a No. 2 pencil. Do NOT use ink.
- Make dark marks and bubble in your answers completely.
- If you change an answer, erase your first mark completely.

Right
(A) (B) (C) (D)

Wrong
(A) (B) (C) (D)
(A) (B) (C) (D)

③ **STUDENT IDENTIFICATION**

| | | | | | | | | |
|---|---|---|---|---|---|---|---|---|
| 0 | 0 | 0 | 0 | 0 | 0 | 0 | 0 | 0 |
| 1 | 1 | 1 | 1 | 1 | 1 | 1 | 1 | 1 |
| 2 | 2 | 2 | 2 | 2 | 2 | 2 | 2 | 2 |
| 3 | 3 | 3 | 3 | 3 | 3 | 3 | 3 | 3 |
| 4 | 4 | 4 | 4 | 4 | 4 | 4 | 4 | 4 |
| 5 | 5 | 5 | 5 | 5 | 5 | 5 | 5 | 5 |
| 6 | 6 | 6 | 6 | 6 | 6 | 6 | 6 | 6 |
| 7 | 7 | 7 | 7 | 7 | 7 | 7 | 7 | 7 |
| 8 | 8 | 8 | 8 | 8 | 8 | 8 | 8 | 8 |
| 9 | 9 | 9 | 9 | 9 | 9 | 9 | 9 | 9 |

**Is this your Social Security number?**
**Yes** ◯ **No** ◯

④ **TEST DATE**

| MM | D | D | Y | Y |
|---|---|---|---|---|
| Jan | 0 | 0 | 200 | 9 |
| Feb | 1 | 1 | 201 | 0 |
| Mar | 2 | 2 | 201 | 1 |
| Apr | 3 | 3 | 201 | 2 |
| May | | 4 | 201 | 3 |
| Jun | | 5 | 201 | 4 |
| Jul | | 6 | 201 | 5 |
| Aug | | 7 | 201 | 6 |
| Sep | | 8 | 201 | 7 |
| Oct | | 9 | 201 | 8 |
| Nov | | | | |
| Dec | | | | |

⑤ **CLASS NUMBER**

| | | | | | | | |
|---|---|---|---|---|---|---|---|
| 0 | 0 | 0 | 0 | 0 | 0 | 0 | 0 |
| 1 | 1 | 1 | 1 | 1 | 1 | 1 | 1 |
| 2 | 2 | 2 | 2 | 2 | 2 | 2 | 2 |
| 3 | 3 | 3 | 3 | 3 | 3 | 3 | 3 |
| 4 | 4 | 4 | 4 | 4 | 4 | 4 | 4 |
| 5 | 5 | 5 | 5 | 5 | 5 | 5 | 5 |
| 6 | 6 | 6 | 6 | 6 | 6 | 6 | 6 |
| 7 | 7 | 7 | 7 | 7 | 7 | 7 | 7 |
| 8 | 8 | 8 | 8 | 8 | 8 | 8 | 8 |
| 9 | 9 | 9 | 9 | 9 | 9 | 9 | 9 |

⑥ **RAW SCORE**

| | |
|---|---|
| 0 | 0 |
| 1 | 1 |
| 2 | 2 |
| 3 | 3 |
| 4 | 4 |
| 5 | 5 |
| 6 | 6 |
| 7 | 7 |
| 8 | 8 |
| 9 | 9 |

© 2010 Pearson Education, Inc. Permission is granted to reproduce for classroom use.

# Future 5 Unit 1 Test Answer Key

| | ANSWER | LESSON/PAGE | OBJECTIVE |
|---|---|---|---|
| 1 | A | 3/p. 10 | Understand a conversation about personality traits |
| 2 | A | 6/p. 16 | Understand a conversation about setting goals |
| 3 | B | 5/p. 14 | Understand a conversation about a person's abilities |
| 4 | C | 7/p. 18 | Understand a conversation about career goals |
| 5 | C | 7/p. 18 | Understand a conversation about career goals |
| 6 | A | 3/p. 10 | Understand a conversation about personality traits |
| 7 | B | 4/p. 12 | Understand a conversation about finding job information |
| 8 | A | 8/p. 20 | Understand a conversation about obstacles to goals |
| 9 | B | 1/p. 6 | Identify job-related interests and abilities |
| 10 | D | 1/p. 6 | Identify job-related interests and abilities |
| 11 | D | 1/p. 6 | Identify job-related interests and abilities |
| 12 | C | 1/p. 6 | Identify job-related interests and abilities |
| 13 | B | 1/p. 6 | Identify job-related interests and abilities |
| 14 | C | 2/p. 8 | Verbs followed by gerunds and/or infinitives |
| 15 | A | 2/p. 8 | Verbs followed by gerunds and/or infinitives |
| 16 | A | 2/p. 8 | Verbs followed by gerunds and/or infinitives |
| 17 | C | 2/p. 8 | Verbs followed by gerunds and/or infinitives |
| 18 | B | 5/p. 14 | Gerunds following prepositions |
| 19 | B | 5/p. 14 | Gerunds following prepositions |
| 20 | A | 5/p. 14 | Gerunds following prepositions |
| 21 | C | 4/p. 12 | Identify the main idea |
| 22 | C | 4/p. 12 | Understand details |
| 23 | D | 4/p. 12 | Understand details |
| 24 | B | 4/p. 12 | Understand details |
| 25 | D | 4/p. 12 | Make inferences |
| 26 | B | 8/p. 20 | Identify the main idea |
| 27 | A | 8/p. 20 | Understand details |
| 28 | B | 8/p. 20 | Understand details |
| 29 | C | 8/p. 20 | Understand details |
| 30 | D | 8/p. 20 | Make inferences |
| 31 | C | 9/p. 22 | Use a topic sentence to state the main idea of a paragraph |
| 32 | A | 9/p. 22 | Use details to support a topic sentence |
| 33 | D | 9/p. 22 | Use details to support a topic sentence |

**Please see reverse for test audio script.**

# Unit 1 Test Audio Script

## **Listening I** (Tracks 3–6) Page 1

**1.** Which personality trait does the man have?

**F:** So, tell me about yourself.
**M:** Well, I'm helpful. I mean, I'm always willing to work with other people and help them.
**F:** OK. Can you give me an example?
**M:** Um, well, sometimes I finish my work early, and then I help my coworkers finish their work.

Which personality trait does the man have?

**2.** What is the woman explaining?

**M:** It seems that you always get what you want. How are you so successful?
**F:** It's about making a commitment to get what you want. First, you need to visualize the outcome you want. Then you need to choose a date by which you will achieve it.

What is the woman explaining?

**3.** What is the woman good at?

**F:** I took an aptitude test at the career center, and I got the results today.
**M:** Oh, yeah? What did you find out?
**F:** Well, the test showed that I like working with people, and I have good communication skills. But I need to improve my problem-solving skills.

What is the woman good at?

**4.** What does the man want to do in the future?

**F:** Hi, Mario. I haven't seen you in a while. What are you doing nowadays?
**M:** Well, I'm working as a restaurant manager, but I'm also taking culinary classes. My goal is to graduate and start my own catering business.

What does the man want to do in the future?

## **Listening II** (Tracks 7–8) Page 1

**5.** **F:** I've been thinking a lot about my career and what I want to do in the future.
**M:** Oh, yeah? What's your long-term career goal?

**6.** **F:** Tell me a little about yourself.
**M:** When I make a decision, I don't just look at the information. It also has to feel right.
**F:** So you trust your feelings when you make your decisions?

## **Listening III** (Tracks 9–10) Page 1

**7.** **M:** So, I hear you're looking for a job. Have you gone on any interviews yet?
**F:** Well, I haven't gone on any actual job interviews. But I've been talking to a career counselor, and she's helped me get some informational interviews.
**M:** That sounds like a good idea. You can learn a lot about a job that way.

Which sentence is true?

8. **F:** Hey, Pablo. How are you? You haven't been to class in a long time.
**M:** I had to drop out. My schedule changed, and now I have to work in the mornings.
**F:** Too bad. But there are classes in the evenings. Maybe you could take one of those.

Which sentence is true?

# Future 5 Unit 2 Test Answer Key

| | ANSWER | LESSON/PAGE | OBJECTIVE |
|---|---|---|---|
| 1 | C | 4/p. 32 | Understand a conversation about interview do's and don'ts |
| 2 | B | 4/p. 32 | Understand a conversation about interview do's and don'ts |
| 3 | C | 3/p. 30 | Understand a conversation about résumé advice |
| 4 | A | 7/p. 38 | Respond to interview questions |
| 5 | B | 5/p. 34 | Respond to interview questions |
| 6 | A | 7/p. 38 | Respond to interview questions |
| 7 | C | 8/p. 40 | Understand a conversation about education and work experience |
| 8 | B | 8/p. 40 | Understand a conversation about education and work experience |
| 9 | A | 2/p. 28 | Analyze résumés |
| 10 | D | 2/p. 28 | Analyze résumés |
| 11 | B | 2/p. 28 | Analyze résumés |
| 12 | A | 2/p. 28 | Analyze résumés |
| 13 | C | 2/p. 28 | Analyze résumés |
| 14 | C | 6/p. 36 | Present perfect |
| 15 | B | 6/p. 36 | Present perfect |
| 16 | A | 6/p. 36 | Present perfect vs. simple past |
| 17 | B | 6/p. 36 | Present perfect |
| 18 | A | 8/p. 40 | Present perfect vs. present perfect continuous |
| 19 | B | 8/p. 40 | Present perfect vs. present perfect continuous |
| 20 | C | 8/p. 40 | Present Perfect vs. present perfect continuous |
| 21 | C | 1/p. 26 | Identify the main idea |
| 22 | B | 1/p. 26 | Make inferences |
| 23 | D | 1/p. 26 | Compare and contrast |
| 24 | C | 1/p. 26 | Understand details |
| 25 | D | 1/p. 26 | Understand details |
| 26 | C | 5/p. 34 | Identify the main idea |
| 27 | B | 5/p. 34 | Understand main idea |
| 28 | A | 5/p. 34 | Compare and contrast |
| 29 | D | 5/p. 34 | Understand details |
| 30 | C | 5/p. 34 | Understand details |
| 31 | D | 9/p. 42 | Highlight key résumé points in a cover letter |
| 32 | C | 9/p. 42 | Use language from a job ad in a cover letter |
| 33 | A | 9/p. 42 | Use language from a job ad in a cover letter |

**Please see reverse for test audio script.**

# Unit 2 Test Audio Script

## **Listening I** (Tracks 11–13) Page 10

1. What is the man's advice?
   **M:** Are you ready for your interview tomorrow?
   **F:** Yes, I've already practiced my answers to a lot of interview questions.
   **M:** Your answers to questions are important, but so are some other things. For example, you need to dress appropriately for the job you want. Depending on the job, business clothes might not be necessary. But you should always have a neat, clean appearance.

   What is the man's advice?

2. What does the woman say?
   **F:** Hey, your interview is this afternoon, isn't it?
   **M:** Yes. I'm almost ready. I'm just preparing a few things.
   **F:** OK. But remember, don't take anything except what you need. And don't forget to turn off your cell phone.

   What does the woman say?

3. What is the woman's advice?
   **F:** Are you still working on your résumé?
   **M:** Yeah. It's hard. I have a lot of information to include.
   **F:** Well, you don't have to include everything. Try to be brief. Your résumé shouldn't be longer than one page.

   What is the woman's advice?

## **Listening II** (Tracks 14–16) Page 10

4. **M:** May I call your references?

5. **F:** So, let's get started. Can you tell me a little about yourself?

6. **M:** Thank you again for coming for the interview today. We'll be making a decision soon. But before we finish, do you have any questions for me?

## **Listening III** (Tracks 17–18) Page 10

7. **F:** Tell me about your work experience.
   **M:** Well, I've been working as a cashier at Green's Supermarket for two years. Before that I was a stock clerk.

   Which sentence is true?

8. **F:** Tell me, why do you think you're qualified for this job?
   **M:** Well, I don't have a lot of work experience, but I believe that my recent job training has prepared me very well for this position.

   Which sentence is true?

# Future 5 Unit 3 Test Answer Key

| | ANSWER | LESSON/PAGE | OBJECTIVE |
|---|---|---|---|
| 1 | B | 2/p. 48 | Understand a conversation about a car breakdown |
| 2 | C | 7/p. 53 | Understand a conversation about traffic problems |
| 3 | C | 2/p. 48 | Understand a conversation about a car breakdown on the highway |
| 4 | B | 1/p. 46 | Listen to a conversation and identify car parts |
| 5 | A | 1/p. 46 | Listen to a conversation and identify car parts |
| 6 | A | 3/p. 50 | Understand a conversation involving highway safety |
| 7 | B | 1/p. 46 | Listen to a conversation and identify car problems |
| 8 | C | 7/p. 53 | Understand a conversation about traffic problems |
| 9 | A | 5/p. 54 | Understand car insurance |
| 10 | B | 1/p. 46 | Identify car parts |
| 11 | A | 8/p. 60 | Use the Internet to get maps and directions |
| 12 | B | 8/p. 60 | Use the Internet to get maps and directions |
| 13 | D | 8/p. 60 | Use the Internet to get maps and directions |
| 14 | A | 3/p. 50 | Inseparable phrasal verbs |
| 15 | B | 3/p. 50 | Inseparable phrasal verbs |
| 16 | A | 3/p. 50 | Separable phrasal verbs |
| 17 | C | 3/p. 50 | Separable phrasal verbs |
| 18 | A | 4/p. 53 | Gerunds and infinitives in general statements |
| 19 | B | 4/p. 53 | Gerunds and infinitives in general statements |
| 20 | B | 4/p. 53 | Gerunds and infinitives in general statements |
| 21 | C | 5/p. 54 | Identify the main idea |
| 22 | A | 3/p. 49 | Paraphrase |
| 23 | C | 5/p. 54 | Understand details |
| 24 | D | 5/p. 54 | Understand details |
| 25 | C | 5/p. 54 | Make inferences |
| 26 | D | 4/p. 52 | Identify the main idea |
| 27 | B | 4/p. 52 | Understand details |
| 28 | B | 6/p. 56 | Understand sequence |
| 29 | C | 6/p. 56 | Understand sequence |
| 30 | C | 4/p. 52 | Make inferences |
| 31 | A | 9/p. 62 | Present a strong argument in a written piece |
| 32 | D | 9/p. 62 | Use details to support an argument |
| 33 | D | 9/p. 62 | Use details to support an argument |

**Please see reverse for test audio script.**

# Unit 3 Test Audio Script

## Listening I (Tracks 19–21) Page 20

1. What does the woman recommend?
   **M:** My car broke down on the interstate yesterday.
   **F:** Oh, no! I'm sorry to hear that. What did you do?
   **M:** Luckily I was able to pull over to the shoulder. Then I called roadside assistance. While I was waiting I tried to flag down some other cars, but no one stopped.
   **F:** You're lucky you weren't hurt. You know, if you ever break down on the highway again you should stay in your car. Wait there for the police or roadside assistance to help.

   What does the woman recommend?

2. What is the woman going to do?
   **F:** Hey, I'm going downtown. Do you need anything?
   **M:** No thanks, but remember, you can't take Morgan Street. The bridge is still closed.
   **F:** OK. Thanks. I'll take one of the detour routes.

   What is the woman going to do?

3. What is the man talking about?

   **M:** If your car breaks down, and you don't have a cellphone, you can get help from other drivers.
   **F:** How? By flagging someone down?
   **M:** No. First put on your emergency flashers. Then, once your car is on the shoulder, set up reflecting triangles behind your car. Next, open the hood of the car, and hang a white cloth out the window.

   What is the man talking about?

## Listening II (Tracks 22–23) Page 20

4. **M:** I almost got into an accident on the way here. It was raining, and I couldn't see anything.
   **F:** Really? It's not raining *that* hard.

5. **F:** My bags are pretty big. Would you mind helping me carry them to the car?
   **M:** Of course not. Where should I put them?

## Listening III (Tracks 24–26) Page 20

6. **F:** One of my tires blew out yesterday while I was on the highway.
   **M:** Really? What did you do?
   **F:** I pulled onto the right shoulder, and I called a friend. She came and helped me change the tire. After that my car was fine, and I drove home.

   Which sentence is true?

7. **F:** Hello, Mike's Mechanics.
   **M:** Hi. I'd like to make an appointment to bring in my car.
   **F:** What's the problem?
   **M:** Well, it's not running very well. And I already changed the oil, so I know that's not the problem.

   Which sentence is true?

8. **F:** What's the fastest way to get to Franklin Park from here?
   **M:** Well, that depends—are you walking or driving?
   **F:** Walking. Why?
   **M:** Well, the fastest way is to cross the Third Street Bridge. It's closed to vehicles for construction, but pedestrians can still use it.

   Which sentence is true?

# Future 5 Unit 4 Test Answer Key

| | ANSWER | LESSON/PAGE | OBJECTIVE |
|---|---|---|---|
| 1 | C | 5/p. 74 | Understand a conversation about keeping latchkey kids safe |
| 2 | A | 1/p. 66 | Understand a conversation about a survivor of a natural disaster |
| 3 | B | 5/p. 74 | Understand a conversation about keeping latchkey kids safe |
| 4 | B | 2/p. 68 | Understand a conversation about tornadoes |
| 5 | A | 6/p. 76 | Identify home safety measures |
| 6 | B | 1/p. 66 | Understand a conversation about natural disasters and their survivors |
| 7 | B | 4/p. 72 | Understand a conversation about mistakes made during emergencies |
| 8 | A | 7/p. 78 | Understand someone reporting a workplace hazard |
| 9 | C | 8/p. 80 | Identify workplace safety measures |
| 10 | B | 6/p. 76 | Identify home safety measures |
| 11 | C | 8/p. 80 | Identify workplace safety measures |
| 12 | D | 6/p. 76 | Identify home safety measures |
| 13 | B | 6/p. 76 | Identify home safety measures |
| 14 | A | 4/p. 72 | Past modals |
| 15 | C | 4/p. 72 | Past modals |
| 16 | A | 4/p. 72 | Past modals |
| 17 | C | 4/p. 72 | Past modals |
| 18 | B | 4/p. 72 | Past modals |
| 19 | B | 4/p. 72 | Past modals |
| 20 | C | 4/p. 72 | Past modals |
| 21 | B | 3/p. 70 | Identify the main idea |
| 22 | C | 3/p. 70 | Understand details |
| 23 | A | 3/p. 70 | Make inferences |
| 24 | B | 3/p. 70 | Make inferences |
| 25 | A | 2/p. 68 | Summarize |
| 26 | D | 2/p. 68 | Identify the main idea |
| 27 | A | 2/p. 68 | Understand sequence |
| 28 | C | 2/p. 68 | Understand details |
| 29 | B | 2/p. 68 | Make inferences |
| 30 | D | 2/p. 68 | Summarize |
| 31 | C | 9/p. 82 | State your topic |
| 32 | A | 9/p. 82 | Use imperatives when giving instructions |
| 33 | D | 9/p. 82 | Use signal words to help readers follow instructions |

**Please see reverse for test audio script.**

# Unit 4 Test Audio Script

## Listening I (Tracks 27–29) Page 30

1. What does Maria's son do after school?
   **M:** Hey, Maria. How are you? I never see you anymore.
   **F:** I know. My work schedule changed. Now I work until 6:00.
   **M:** And what about your son? What does he do after school?
   **F:** Well, at first that was a problem. He's too old to go to a babysitter's house, but I didn't want him to be at home alone either. So I found out about the school's after-school activities. They offer sports and other programs in the afternoons. So now he stays at school until I finish work.

   What does Maria's son do after school?

2. Who is Katsu Nakamura?
   **M:** I heard a really interesting story about a guy named Katsu Nakamura. He was trapped under rubble during Tuesday's earthquake. He was finally rescued yesterday.
   **F:** Yesterday? That means he was trapped for three days!
   **M:** I know. It's an incredible story. A police officer heard him calling for help. Then rescuers worked for ten hours to finally free him.

   Who is Katsu Nakamura?

3. What can the man's daughter do if there's a problem?
   **F:** What does your daughter do after school while you're at work?
   **M:** She's at home.
   **F:** Are you worried about her?
   **M:** Well, sometimes, of course. But she's a good kid. And my neighbor is always around. My daughter can always call her if there's a problem.

   What can the man's daughter do if there's a problem?

## Listening II (Tracks 30–31) Page 30

4. **F:** Did you hear that? They just said on TV there's a tornado watch.
   **M:** What does that mean?

5. **F1:** I was so scared this morning. My five-year-old son almost fell out of his bedroom window.
   **F2:** How frightening. Is he OK?
   **F1:** He's fine, but I'm nervous. What if it happens again?

## Listening III (Tracks 32–34) Page 30

6. **F:** Did you hear—there was a small earthquake in Mexico yesterday.
   **M:** Really? I didn't hear about it. What happened?
   **F:** Well, it wasn't very strong. And it was in an area where there aren't a lot of people. So luckily, no one was hurt.

   Which sentence is true?

7. **F:** OK. Are we ready to go?
   **M:** Yes, I think so. We just need to stop at the gas station on our way.
   **F:** What? We still need to put gas in the car? You should have done that earlier.
   **M:** I thought about it, but the lines were really long.
   **F:** Well, now they're going to be even longer!

   Which sentence is true?

8. **F:** Excuse me, Mr. Chen? I'd like to talk to you—it's about a hazard in the warehouse.
   **M:** OK.
   **F:** Well, the lighting in there is really bad. It's hard to see. And especially when the other workers and I are carrying big boxes, that can be dangerous. It's easy to trip and fall.
   **M:** Well, thank you for telling me. I'll look into the problem.

   Which sentence is true?

# Future 5 Unit 5 Test Answer Key

| | ANSWER | LESSON/PAGE | OBJECTIVE |
|---|---|---|---|
| 1 | B | 4/p. 92 | Understand a conversation about job performance and promotions |
| 2 | A | 5/p. 94 | Understand a conversation about job-training opportunities |
| 3 | A | 3/p. 90 | Understand constructive criticism |
| 4 | B | 8/p. 100 | Understand how to use common workplace idioms from sports |
| 5 | C | 3/p. 90 | Understand how to respond to constructive criticism |
| 6 | B | 8/p. 100 | Understand common workplace idioms from sports |
| 7 | A | 7/p. 98 | Understand the difference between *I* and *you* statements |
| 8 | C | 5/p. 94 | Understand a conversation about job-training opportunities |
| 9 | A | 6/p. 96 | Use a course catalog |
| 10 | D | 6/p. 96 | Use a course catalog |
| 11 | B | 6/p. 96 | Use a course catalog |
| 12 | D | 6/p. 96 | Use a course catalog |
| 13 | B | 6/p. 96 | Use a course catalog |
| 14 | A | 4/p. 92 | Clauses with *although* and *unless* |
| 15 | B | 4/p. 92 | Clauses with *although* and *unless* |
| 16 | A | 4/p. 92 | Clauses with *although* and *unless* |
| 17 | B | 4/p. 92 | Clauses with *although* and *unless* |
| 18 | C | 4/p. 92 | Clauses with *although* and *unless* |
| 19 | C | 4/p. 92 | Clauses with *although* and *unless* |
| 20 | A | 4/p. 92 | Clauses with *although* and *unless* |
| 21 | D | 1/p. 86 | Identify the main idea |
| 22 | C | 1/p. 86 | Understand details |
| 23 | B | 1/p. 86 | Identify the main idea |
| 24 | C | 1/p. 86 | Make inferences |
| 25 | D | 1/p. 86 | Understand details |
| 26 | D | 1 p. 86 | Identify the main idea |
| 27 | A | 2/p. 88 | Understand details |
| 28 | B | 2/p. 88 | Understand details |
| 29 | C | 1/p. 86 | Identify the main idea |
| 30 | D | 2/p. 88 | Make inferences |
| 31 | B | 9/p. 102 | Use examples to support your self-assessment |
| 32 | B | 9/p. 102 | Use examples to support your self-assessment |
| 33 | D | 9/p. 102 | In multiple paragraph writing, group similar ideas together in each paragraph |

**Please see reverse for test audio script.**

# Unit 5 Test Audio Script

## Listening I (Tracks 35–37) Page 39

1. What will happen if the man doesn't get a promotion?
   **F:** So, how are things at work?
   **M:** Actually, I'm hoping to get a promotion. I've been taking some classes, and I'm ready for a new challenge.
   **F:** Well, you always get good performance reviews. You deserve a promotion.
   **M:** I agree. So unless I get a promotion, I'm going to leave the company.

   What will happen if the man doesn't get a promotion?

2. What is the man going to do?
   **F:** So, how's work going?
   **M:** Really well, actually. My boss said he thinks I'm ready for more responsibility at work. So I'm going to get some on-the-job training. That will help me get some of the skills I'll need for a promotion.

   What is the man going to do?

3. What's the problem?
   **M:** Can you tell me why I got a 3 in quality of work? I always finish my work, and it's always on time.
   **F:** That's true, but sometimes there are mistakes in your work. It's important your work be on-time *and* accurate. You're a good employee, and you have a very positive attitude. But you need to pay more attention to details.
   **M:** Thank you for explaining it to me. I understand.

   What's the problem?

## Listening II (Tracks 38–39) Page 39

4. **F:** So how's the new project at work going?
   **M:** It's great so far.
   **F:** I'm glad to hear it. Who's in charge of the project? Is it Mike?

5. **F:** Do you have any questions about the ratings on your performance review?
   **M:** Well, I don't understand why I got a 2 in problem solving.
   **F:** You have very good ideas, but a lot of times you don't share them with your team. You need to offer your suggestions in group discussions.

## Listening III (Tracks 40–42) Page 39

6. **F:** Hey, I heard you applied for the manager position. That's great.
   **M:** Thanks. I'd love to get the job, but it's a long shot.

   Which sentence is true?

7. **F:** Excuse me, Marco. Would you mind turning down your music? I have to finish this report, and I need to concentrate.
   **M:** Oh, sure. Sorry about that.

   Which sentence is true?

8. **F:** Today my supervisor told me that he thinks I would be a good assistant manager.
   **M:** That's great!
   **F:** Well, he also said I need to improve my communication skills. The community college offers a career training course, so I'm going to look into that.

   Which sentence is true?

# Future 5 Unit 6 Test Answer Key

| | ANSWER | LESSON/PAGE | OBJECTIVE |
|---|---|---|---|
| 1 | B | 8/p. 120 | Understand a conversation about diabetes |
| 2 | A | 6/p. 116 | Understand a conversation about preventive health care |
| 3 | B | 7/p. 118 | Understand a conversation about preventive health care |
| 4 | C | 7/p. 118 | Understand a conversation about preventive health care |
| 5 | A | 5/p. 114 | Interpret casual questions about health |
| 6 | B | 2/p. 108 | Understand a description of medical problems |
| 7 | B | 3/p. 110 | Listen to a conversation about taking medication properly |
| 8 | C | 2/p. 108 | Understand what someone needs to do for a medical problem |
| 9 | A | 3/p. 110 | Identify how to take medication properly |
| 10 | D | 3/p. 110 | Identify how to take medication properly |
| 11 | B | 3/p. 110 | Identify how to take medication properly |
| 12 | C | 3/p. 110 | Identify how to take medication properly |
| 13 | B | 3/p. 110 | Identify how to take medication properly |
| 14 | B | 6/p. 116 | Embedded *Wh-* questions |
| 15 | A | 6/p. 116 | Embedded *Yes/No* questions |
| 16 | C | 6/p. 116 | Embedded *Wh-* questions |
| 17 | A | 6/p. 116 | Embedded *Yes/No* questions |
| 18 | A | 6/p. 116 | Embedded *Wh-* questions |
| 19 | B | 6/p. 116 | Embedded *Wh-* questions |
| 20 | C | 6/p. 116 | Embedded *Yes/No* questions |
| 21 | C | 4/p. 112 | Identify the main idea |
| 22 | A | 7/p. 118 | Recognize cause and effect |
| 23 | C | 4/p. 112 | Understand a sequence |
| 24 | B | 4/p. 112 | Understand details |
| 25 | D | 4/p. 112 | Make inferences |
| 26 | C | 1/p. 106 | Identify the main idea |
| 27 | A | 7/p. 118 | Recognize cause and effect |
| 28 | C | 1/p. 106 | Understand details |
| 29 | D | 1/p. 106 | Understand details |
| 30 | C | 1/p. 106 | Make inferences |
| 31 | A | 9/p. 122 | Write a strong introductory paragraph |
| 32 | A | 9/p. 122 | Write a strong introductory paragraph |
| 33 | A | 9/p. 122 | Support arguments with examples |

**Please see reverse for test audio script.**

# Unit 6 Test Audio Script

## Listening I (Tracks 43–45) Page 49

1. What does the woman say?
   **F:** They're doing free diabetes screenings today at the community center. You should go.
   **M:** Me? Why?
   **F:** Well, your father has diabetes, and since you have a family history, you're at risk for getting it. Plus, you don't exercise a lot, and that's a risk factor, too.

   What does the woman say?

2. What does the woman want to know?
   **F:** Could you tell me what I can do to lower my blood pressure? Should I take medicine?
   **M:** Well, medication is one option, but first you should try some other things. You can make big changes to your blood pressure by changing your diet.

   What does the woman want to know?

3. Why is the man going to Drug Smart?
   **F:** Where are you going?
   **M:** To Drug Smart. They're doing free cholesterol screenings this afternoon.
   **F:** But you don't have high cholesterol, do you?
   **M:** I don't know, but my mother does. And since I have a family history, I should get checked.

   Why is the man going to Drug Smart?

## Listening II (Tracks 46–47) Page 49

4. **M:** Wow, you use a lot of salt on your food. Do you have high blood pressure?
   **F:** I don't know—why?
   **M:** Well, salt can raise your blood pressure, and if you already have high blood pressure, that could cause serious health problems for you.
   **F:** So how do I know if my blood pressure is too high?

5. **F:** Hey, Steven. How are you?
   **M:** Fine, thanks. And you?

## Listening III (Tracks 48–50) Page 49

6. **F:** Do you want to go to the library with me after class today?
   **M:** Sorry, I have an appointment with the dermatologist.
   **F:** I hope it's nothing serious.
   **M:** I don't think it is. But my legs have these little bumps on them, and the skin is really red and itchy, so I thought I should have the doctor take a look at them.

   Which sentence is true?

7. **F:** How should I take this medicine, and for how long should I take it?
   **M:** Take one pill a day in the morning after breakfast. Take all the medicine until it's gone, even if you feel better.

   Which sentence is true?

8. **M:** What's your doctor's appointment for?
   **F:** I've been having chest pains, and my doctor recommended that I see a specialist. So I have an appointment with a cardiologist.

   Which sentence is true?

# Future 5 Unit 7 Test Answer Key

| | ANSWER | LESSON/PAGE | OBJECTIVE |
|---|---|---|---|
| 1 | C | 4/p. 132 | Understand a conversation about individual rights in the Constitution |
| 2 | C | 2/p. 128 | Understand a conversation about the early history of the U.S. |
| 3 | B | 6/p. 136 | Understand a conversation about the benefits of U.S. citizenship |
| 4 | B | 1/p. 126 | Understand a conversation about the beginnings of the U.S. |
| 5 | A | 5/p. 134 | Understand a conversation about how a bill becomes a law |
| 6 | C | 7/p. 138 | Understand a conversation about becoming a U.S. citizen |
| 7 | A | 5/p. 135 | Understand a conversation about the U.S. government |
| 8 | C | 6/p. 136 | Understand a conversation about the benefits of U.S. citizenship |
| 9 | D | 8/p. 140 | Interpret a map of the U.S. |
| 10 | C | 8/p. 140 | Interpret a map of the U.S. |
| 11 | A | 8/p. 140 | Interpret a map of the U.S. |
| 12 | C | 8/p. 140 | Interpret a map of the U.S. |
| 13 | D | 8/p. 140 | Interpret a map of the U.S. |
| 14 | B | 2/p. 128 | Past perfect |
| 15 | C | 2/p. 128 | Past perfect |
| 16 | A | 5/p. 135 | Passives with *get* |
| 17 | C | 5/p. 135 | Passives with *get* |
| 18 | B | 2/p. 128 | Past perfect |
| 19 | C | 5/p. 135 | Passives with *get* |
| 20 | A | 2/p. 128 | Past perfect |
| 21 | B | 3/p. 130 | Identify the main idea |
| 22 | C | 6/p. 136 | Use text structure and formatting |
| 23 | D | 5/p. 134 | Understand details |
| 24 | B | 3/p. 130 | Understand details |
| 25 | A | 5/p. 134 | Make inferences |
| 26 | B | 7/p. 138 | Identify the main idea |
| 27 | C | 6/p. 136 | Use text structure and formatting |
| 28 | D | 7/p. 138 | Understand details |
| 29 | D | 7/p. 138 | Understand details |
| 30 | B | 7/p. 138 | Make inferences |
| 31 | A | 9/p. 142 | Use a problem/solution structure |
| 32 | C | 9/p. 142 | Use a problem/solution structure |
| 33 | B | 9/p. 142 | End your e-mail in a polite, diplomatic way |

**Please see reverse for test audio script.**

# Unit 7 Test Audio Script

## **Listening I** (Tracks 51–54) Page 59

1. Who does the amendment protect?
   **M:** The First Amendment guarantees freedom of religion in the U.S.
   **F:** But that's only for citizens, right?
   **M:** No, the First Amendment is part of the Bill of Rights, which protects the rights of U.S. citizens *and* the rights of non-citizens, residents, and visitors to this country.

   Who does the amendment protect?

2. What happened first?
   **F:** I know the English, the French, and the Spanish all settled different parts of North America. Did they all arrive around the same time?
   **M:** No. By the time the English and French settlers arrived, the Spanish had already arrived and started to explore North America.

   What happened first?

3. Why is the woman excited?
   **F:** This is the first national election since I became a U.S. citizen.
   **M:** Are you going to vote?
   **F:** Of course! I'm so excited to vote in the U.S.

   Why is the woman excited?

4. Where were wheat and corn grown?

   **M:** I know that in colonies like Virginia the settlers grew tobacco to make money. Did most of the settlers make their living this way?
   **F:** No. Most of the people in the New England colonies like Massachusetts and New Hampshire were farmers, but they grew things like wheat and corn. They sent a lot of it to England.

   Where were wheat and corn grown?

## **Listening II** (Tracks 55–58) Page 59

5. **M:** Did you hear that the House passed the new bill on education today?
   **F:** No, but that's great! And the Senate already passed it, too, right?
   **M:** Yeah. Now it goes to the President. I hope he signs it.

   Which sentence is true?

6. **F:** You've been in the U.S. for a while now, haven't you?
   **M:** Yeah, I've been here for eight years.
   **F:** You only need to be here for five before you can apply for citizenship. And you have an I-551 card. Why don't you apply?
   **M:** Well, you need to have lived here as a *permanent resident* for five years. I've only been a permanent resident for four.
   **F:** Oh, so you have to wait another year.

   Which sentence is true?

7. **F:** I heard on the news that Joan Nelson got elected to the Senate.
   **M:** That's great news! I think she'll help pass some important bills.

   Which sentence is true?

8. **F:** How long have you lived in the U.S.?
   **M:** Ten years.
   **F:** Wow. Does the rest of your family live here, too?
   **M:** No, they're in Peru. But since I'm a U.S. citizen now, I'm going to try to bring them to the U.S.

   Which sentence is true?

# Future 5 Unit 8 Test Answer Key

| | ANSWER | LESSON/PAGE | OBJECTIVE |
|---|---|---|---|
| 1 | C | 2/p. 148 | Understand a conversation about traffic tickets |
| 2 | B | 1/p. 146 | Understand a conversation about rights of people accused of crimes |
| 3 | A | 5/p. 154 | Understand a conversation about laws protecting children |
| 4 | A | 6/p. 156 | Understand a conversation about traffic court |
| 5 | C | 3/p. 150 | Understand a conversation about the right to vote |
| 6 | A | 4/p. 152 | Understand a conversation about sexual harassment in the workplace |
| 7 | C | 7/p. 158 | Understand a conversation about types of crimes |
| 8 | B | 8/p. 160 | Understand a conversation about why fines can be serious |
| 9 | A | 4/p. 152 | Recognize sexual harassment in the workplace |
| 10 | D | 4/p. 152 | Recognize sexual harassment in the workplace |
| 11 | C | 4/p. 152 | Recognize sexual harassment in the workplace |
| 12 | B | 4/p. 152 | Recognize sexual harassment in the workplace |
| 13 | C | 4/p. 152 | Recognize sexual harassment in the workplace |
| 14 | A | 2/p. 148 | Future real conditional |
| 15 | C | 2/p. 148 | Future real conditional |
| 16 | A | 2/p. 148 | Future real conditional |
| 17 | C | 2/p. 148 | Future real conditional |
| 18 | B | 2/p. 148 | Future real conditional |
| 19 | B | 2/p. 148 | Future real conditional |
| 20 | A | 2/p. 148 | Future real conditional |
| 21 | C | 3/p. 150 | Identify the main idea |
| 22 | D | 3/p. 150 | Understand details |
| 23 | A | 3/p. 150 | Distinguish fact from opinion |
| 24 | B | 6/p. 156 | Make inferences |
| 25 | C | 6/p. 156 | Make inferences |
| 26 | C | 5/p. 154 | Identify the main idea |
| 27 | A | 5/p. 154 | Understand details |
| 28 | B | 3/p. 150 | Distinguish fact from opinion |
| 29 | D | 5/p. 154 | Understand details |
| 30 | A | 6/p. 156 | Make inferences |
| 31 | B | 9/p. 162 | Describe similarities and differences |
| 32 | C | 9/p. 162 | Describe similarities and differences |
| 33 | D | 9/p. 162 | Structure an essay in a simple and logical way |

**Please see reverse for test audio script.**

# Unit 8 Test Audio Script

## **Listening I** (Tracks 59–62) Page 69

1. What has happened to the woman?
   **M:** Be careful driving. And don't speed on the highway. I saw that there are a lot of police out tonight.
   **F:** Thanks, but don't worry—I won't speed. If I get another ticket, I'll have to go to traffic school because I've already gotten two tickets this year!

   What has happened to the woman?

2. Which right does the woman explain to the man?
   **F:** You have the right to consult an attorney before speaking to the police and to have an attorney present during questioning now or in the future. Do you understand?
   **M:** Yes, I do.

   Which right does the woman explain to the man?

3. What's happening with the case now?
   **F:** Did you hear about those poor children who were sick and left at home alone for three days?
   **M:** Yes, it was such a terrible story. I can't imagine parents neglecting their children like that.
   **F:** I know. I heard the CPS is investigating the case. I hope the parents go to jail.

   What's happening with the case now?

4. What is the man going to do?
   **M:** I got a speeding ticket yesterday. So now I have to pay a fine, right?
   **F:** Let me see the ticket . . . Well, it says you can pay the fine for the ticket, or you can request a trial.
   **M:** I can request a trial?
   **F:** Yes, if you believe you're not guilty you can fight the ticket in court.
   **M:** Oh, well, I *was* speeding, so I guess I'll just pay the fine.

   What is the man going to do?

## **Listening II** (Tracks 63–66) Page 69

5. **F:** Hey, Jeff! Don't forget to vote today!
   **M:** I wish I could vote, but I'm too young. I'm only 17.
   **F:** Oh, too bad.
   **M:** Yeah. But I'll definitely vote in the next election!

   Which sentence is true?

6. **F:** You know my boss, Carl? Well, he's asked me to go on a date a few times. I said no, and I really don't want to. But he said he might not give me a good evaluation if I don't say yes.
   **M:** That's sexual harassment, and it's illegal. You should report your boss to the HR department.

   Which sentence is true?

7. **F:** My son got into some trouble last night.
   **M:** Uh-oh. What happened?
   **F:** He was trespassing on someone's property with some friends from school.
   **M:** Well, that's not good news. But at least it's a misdemeanor, so there won't be a big penalty. If this is his first offense, he'll probably have to pay a fine or do community service.

   Which sentence is true?

8. **F:** Another overdue notice from the library! I wish they would stop bothering me!
   **M:** Why don't you just return the book?
   **F:** Actually, I lost the book, so I can't.
   **M:** In that case you should go to the library and explain the situation. You'll probably have to pay for the book, but that's better than getting a citation.

   Which sentence is true?

# Future 5 Unit 9 Test Answer Key

| | ANSWER | LESSON/PAGE | OBJECTIVE |
|---|---|---|---|
| 1 | B | 2/p. 168 | Understand a conversation about recycling rules |
| 2 | C | 1/p. 166 | Understand a conversation about saving energy and money |
| 3 | A | 5/p. 174 | Understand a conversation about causes and effects of environmental problems |
| 4 | B | 6/p. 176 | Understand a conversation about recycling and reusing things |
| 5 | C | 3/p. 170 | Understand a conversation about carpooling |
| 6 | B | 4/p. 172 | Understand a conversation about recycling in different places |
| 7 | C | 7/p. 178 | Understand a conversation about a way to protect the environment |
| 8 | C | 8/p. 180 | Understand a conversation about how to "green" an area |
| 9 | D | 2/p. 168 | Interpret recycling rules |
| 10 | A | 2/p. 168 | Interpret recycling rules |
| 11 | D | 2/p. 168 | Interpret recycling rules |
| 12 | C | 2/p. 168 | Interpret recycling rules |
| 13 | B | 2/p. 168 | Interpret recycling rules |
| 14 | A | 7/p. 178 | Past subjunctive with *wish* |
| 15 | C | 7/p. 178 | Past unreal conditional |
| 16 | B | 7/p. 178 | Past subjunctive with *wish* |
| 17 | B | 7/p. 178 | Past unreal conditional |
| 18 | C | 7/p. 178 | Past subjunctive with *wish* |
| 19 | B | 7/p. 178 | Past unreal conditional |
| 20 | A | 7/p. 178 | Past unreal conditional |
| 21 | C | 1/p. 166 | Identify the main idea |
| 22 | C | 1/p. 166 | Understand details |
| 23 | D | 4/p. 172 | Understand the style and structure of blogs |
| 24 | B | 8/p. 180 | Use visuals and make an inference |
| 25 | B | 1/p. 166 | Make inferences |
| 26 | D | 8/p. 180 | Identify the main idea |
| 27 | B | 8/p. 180 | Identify supporting details |
| 28 | A | 8/p. 180 | Make inferences |
| 29 | A | 8/p. 180 | Understand details |
| 30 | C | 8/p. 180 | Use visuals and make an inference |
| 31 | C | 9/p. 182 | Use words to show time order |
| 32 | A | 9/p. 182 | Use words to show time order |
| 33 | B | 9/p. 182 | Use words to show time order |

**Please see reverse for test audio script.**

# Unit 9 Test Audio Script

## Listening I (Tracks 67–70) Page 79

1. What is collected today?
   **M:** I have to put out the trash this morning, right?
   **F:** No, trash is tomorrow. Today is recycling.
   **M:** Oh. Which recycling is it today—paper or metal, glass, and plastic?
   **F:** Paper. And will you put this newspaper in there too, please?
   What is collected today?

2. What are the people going to do?
   **F:** You know, we should get some of those energy-efficient lightbulbs.
   **M:** But they cost more than regular lightbulbs, don't they?
   **F:** The price is higher, yes, but they last a lot longer than regular lightbulbs, so you don't have to replace them as often. They use less energy, too. In the end they'll save us money.
   **M:** OK. Let's get some.
   What are the people going to do?

3. What does the woman explain?
   **M:** You know, I don't really understand why people are so worried about cutting down trees. I mean, there are a lot bigger environmental problems to worry about, aren't there?
   **F:** Well, cutting down a tree causes two problems: First, the tree can't absorb carbon dioxide from the air. And secondly, as the tree decays, it adds new carbon dioxide to the air.
   What does the woman explain?

4. What is the man going to do?
   **M:** Hey, if you're not going to use those boxes, can I have them? I'm moving soon.
   **F:** Sure. I was just going to recycle them.
   **M:** Great. I'll need some boxes, and I'd rather reuse old ones instead of buying new ones.
   **F:** Of course. That's a great idea.
   What is the man going to do?

## Listening II (Tracks 71–74) Page 79

5. **F:** I can't believe how much money I spend on gas. It's ridiculous!
   **M:** Well, why don't you try carpooling to work? You'd save a lot in gas money. And I think Alicia Jones lives near you, so it would be convenient.
   **F:** I know, but I really don't want to have to talk to someone every morning. I enjoy being quiet.
   **M:** That shouldn't be a problem. Alicia is pretty quiet.
   **F:** Well, maybe. I'll have to think about it.
   Which sentence is true?

6. **M:** Washington, D.C. is really environmentally friendly.
   **F:** Oh, really?
   **M:** Yeah. For example, you can recycle anything there, including all kinds of plastic.
   **F:** I wish our city were more like that!
   Which sentence is true?

7. **F:** Hey Steve, have you lost weight?
   **M:** Yeah. I've been riding my bike to work. It's great exercise, and I'm saving money on gas.
   **F:** Wow, that's great. And of course you're helping the environment, too.
   Which sentence is true?

8. **M:** I'm thinking about planting some new trees in the garden.
   **F:** That's a great idea. They could provide some shade and keep the house cooler.
   **M:** Yeah, but I don't really know what kind to choose. Do you have any suggestions?
   **F:** You should check out native plants, because they don't need as much watering as other kinds.
   Which sentence is true?

# Future 5 Unit 10 Test Answer Key

| | ANSWER | LESSON/PAGE | OBJECTIVE |
|---|---|---|---|
| 1 | A | 6/p. 196 | Understand references to everyday technology |
| 2 | C | 3/p. 190 | Understand a conversation about the pros and cons of the Internet |
| 3 | B | 5/p. 194 | Understand a conversation about virtual training |
| 4 | A | 8/p. 200 | Understand a conversation about computer training |
| 5 | B | 6/p. 196 | Understand references to everyday technology |
| 6 | C | 8/p. 200 | Understand a conversation about computer training |
| 7 | A | 3/p. 191 | Understand expressions of agreement and disagreement |
| 8 | C | 1/p. 186 | Understand a conversation about the growth of the Internet |
| 9 | A | 2/p. 188 | Understand how to use an instruction manual |
| 10 | C | 2/p. 188 | Understand how to use an instruction manual |
| 11 | B | 2/p. 188 | Understand how to use an instruction manual |
| 12 | A | 2/p. 188 | Understand how to use an instruction manual |
| 13 | C | 2/p. 188 | Understand how to use an instruction manual |
| 14 | A | 5/p. 194 | Adjective clauses |
| 15 | B | 5/p. 194 | Adjective clauses |
| 16 | C | 5/p. 194 | Adjective clauses |
| 17 | A | 5/p. 194 | Adjective clauses |
| 18 | C | 5/p. 194 | Adjective clauses |
| 19 | B | 5/p. 194 | Adjective clauses |
| 20 | B | 5/p. 194 | Adjective clauses |
| 21 | A | 4/p. 192 | Identify author's purpose |
| 22 | C | 4/p. 192 | Identify the main idea |
| 23 | C | 4/p. 192 | Understand details |
| 24 | D | 4/p. 192 | Understand details |
| 25 | B | 4/p. 192 | Make inferences |
| 26 | C | 4/p. 192 | Identify author's purpose |
| 27 | B | 7/p. 198 | Use a time line |
| 28 | C | 7/p. 198 | Understand details |
| 29 | D | 7/p. 198 | Identify the main idea |
| 30 | A | 7/p. 198 | Make inferences |
| 31 | C | 9/p. 202 | Use sensory details |
| 32 | A | 9/p. 202 | Use sensory details |
| 33 | B | 9/p. 202 | Use sensory details |

**Please see reverse for test audio script.**

# Unit 10 Test Audio Script

## Listening I (Tracks 75–78) Page 89

1. What does the woman suggest?
   **F:** Who are you texting?
   **M:** Aldo. I'm telling him not to be late.
   **F:** Why are you spelling out all the letters? You can just write D-N-B-L-8.
   **M:** I know, but I don't like doing that. Maybe I'm old-fashioned, but I'd rather write correctly.
   What does the woman suggest?

2. What does the man think of the Internet?
   **M:** I think the Internet is great. I use it a lot myself. But I worry about the harm it's doing, too.
   **F:** What do you mean?
   **M:** Well, some kids spend all day on the computer. It's not healthy.
   What does the man think of the Internet?

3. What did the man do today?
   **F:** So how was your first day of work?
   **M:** It was fun. I played computer games all day!
   **F:** What are you talking about?
   **M:** It's part of the company's new training program. Instead of making new employees read manuals or watch boring videos, they use virtual training computer games.
   What did the man do today?

4. What does the man suggest?
   **M:** I looked for the Brown Company file on your computer yesterday, but I couldn't find it.
   **F:** Hold on . . . Here it is.
   **M:** Oh, I guess I didn't understand your naming system. Maybe we can agree on a system so we can both find things if we need to.
   **F:** Sure. That sounds like a good idea.
   What does the man suggest?

## Listening II (Tracks 79–82) Page 89

5. **M:** Do you want to do something this evening?
   **F:** Sure. I'm supposed to see Harry, but we can all hang out together.
   **M:** Sounds good. Do you want to call him to make a plan?
   **F:** OK . . . Oh, wait—I just got a text message from him. He'll be here in a minute.
   Which sentence is true?

6. **M:** I signed up for a computer-training course at work today. I think it will help me get some of the basic computer skills I'll need to move up in the company.
   **F:** That's great. What kinds of things are you going to learn?
   **M:** It's pretty basic stuff: creating and saving documents, file management, those sorts of things.
   Which sentence is true?

7. **F:** I don't think students should be allowed to have cell phones at school. And they definitely shouldn't be allowed to use them during school hours.
   **M:** I couldn't agree with you more.
   Which sentence is true?

8. **M:** I can't imagine how we ever lived without the Internet.
   **F:** I know. It's great! It makes so many things faster and easier.
   **M:** And it's amazing how quickly people have gotten used to it.
   **F:** I know. At first I was afraid to try it until my kids showed me how.
   Which sentence is true?

To use the *Future* **Exam***View*® *Assessment Suite*, your computer must meet or exceed the following requirements:

***For Windows®:***

- Intel Pentium® II 120 MHz or compatible processor
- Microsoft Windows® 2000/XP/Vista

***For Macintosh®:***

- Power PC® 120 MHz or higher processor
- Mac OS X (10.2 or later)

***Both:***

- 100 MB of available hard drive space
- 128 MB of available RAM (256 MB recommended)
- Monitor capable of displaying 16-bit color with 800 x 600 resolution
- Internet connection to access test-hosting features, and for Content Update Feature
- CD-ROM Drive

These instructions are for **Exam***View* *Test Generator* version 6. If you have an earlier version of **Exam***View* installed on your computer, it will automatically be replaced by this version when you install it. You can then create all your new tests in this version. If you open an existing test or question bank created with the earlier version, it will automatically be updated.

***For Windows®:***

1. Close all other programs before you begin the installation.
2. Insert the **Exam***View* disc into the CD-ROM drive of your computer.
3. You may be prompted by the computer to open the disc. If this doesn't happen, open **My Computer**.
4. Double-click on the CD-ROM drive icon.

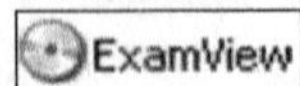


5. Double click on the TO THE TEACHER document in order to read it. This document will instruct you in the best practices to use the *Future* **Exam***View* *Assessment Suite* products. The document will also provide instructions for using the listening portions of the *Future* **Exam***View* tests.
6. After closing the TO THE TEACHER document, double click on the **SETUP** file and follow the instructions on the screen.
7. When the installation is complete, remove the **Exam***View* disc from the CD-ROM drive of your computer.

***For Macintosh®:***

1. Close all other programs before you begin the installation.
2. Insert the **Exam***View* disc into the CD-ROM drive of your computer.
3. Double-click on the **Exam***View* icon that appears on the desktop.
4. Double click on the TO THE TEACHER document in order to read it. This document will instruct you in the best practices to use the *Future* **Exam***View* *Assessment Suite* products. The document will also provide instructions for using the listening portions of the *Future* **Exam***View* tests.
5. After closing the TO THE TEACHER document, double click on the **Exam***View* installer icon and follow the instructions on the screen.
6. When installation is complete, remove the **Exam***View* disc from the CD-ROM drive of your computer.

---

**SINGLE PC LICENSE AGREEMENT AND LIMITED WARRANTY**

**READ THIS LICENSE CAREFULLY BEFORE USING THIS PACKAGE.** BY USING THIS PACKAGE, YOU ARE AGREEING TO THE TERMS AND CONDITIONS OF THIS LICENSE. IF YOU DO NOT AGREE, DO NOT USE THE PACKAGE. PROMPTLY RETURN THE PACKAGE AND ALL ACCOMPANYING ITEMS TO THE PLACE YOU OBTAINED THEM. ***THESE TERMS APPLY TO ALL LICENSED SOFTWARE ON THE DISK EXCEPT THAT THE TERMS FOR USE OF ANY SHAREWARE OR FREEWARE ON THE DISKETTES ARE AS SET FORTH IN THE ELECTRONIC LICENSE LOCATED ON THE DISK:***

**1. GRANT OF LICENSE and OWNERSHIP:** The enclosed computer programs and data ("Software") are licensed, not sold, to you by Pearson Education, Inc. publishing as Pearson Longman ("We" or the "Company") and in consideration of your payment of the license fee, which is part of the price you paid or of your purchase or adoption of the accompanying Company textbooks and/or other materials, and your agreement to these terms. We reserve any rights not granted to you. You own only the disk(s) but we and/or our licensors own the Software itself. This license allows you to use and display your copy of the Software on a single computer (i.e., with a single CPU) at a single location for academic use only, so long as you comply with the terms of this Agreement. You may make one copy for back up, or transfer your copy to another CPU, provided that the Software is usable on only one computer.

**2. RESTRICTIONS:** You may not transfer or distribute the Software or documentation to anyone else. Except for backup, you may not copy the documentation or the Software. You may not network the Software or otherwise use it on more than one computer or computer terminal at the same time. Except as you are otherwise expressly permitted in writing by Pearson, you may not reverse engineer, disassemble, decompile, modify, adapt, translate, or create derivative works based on the Software or the Documentation. You may be held legally responsible for any copying or copyright infringement that is caused by your failure to abide by the terms of these restrictions.

**3. TERMINATION:** This license is effective until terminated. This license will terminate automatically without notice from the Company if you fail to comply with any provisions or limitations of this license. Upon termination, you shall destroy the Documentation and all copies of the Software. All provisions of this Agreement as to limitation and disclaimer of warranties, limitation of liability, remedies or damages, and our ownership rights shall survive termination.

**4. LIMITED WARRANTY AND DISCLAIMER OF WARRANTY:** Company warrants that for a period of 60 days from the date you purchase this SOFTWARE (or purchase or adopt the accompanying textbook), the Software, when properly installed and used in accordance with the Documentation, will operate in substantial conformity with the description of the Software set forth in the Documentation, and that for a period of 30 days the disk(s) on which the Software is delivered shall be free from defects in materials and workmanship under normal use. The Company does not warrant that the Software will meet your requirements or that the operation of the Software will be uninterrupted or error-free. Your only remedy and the Company's only obligation under these limited warranties is, at the Company's option, return of the disk for a refund of any amounts paid for it by you or replacement of the disk. THIS LIMITED WARRANTY IS THE ONLY WARRANTY PROVIDED BY THE COMPANY AND ITS LICENSORS, AND THE COMPANY AND ITS LICENSORS DISCLAIM ALL OTHER WARRANTIES, EXPRESS OR IMPLIED, INCLUDING WITHOUT LIMITATION, THE IMPLIED WARRANTIES OF MERCHANTABILITY AND FITNESS FOR A PARTICULAR PURPOSE. THE COMPANY DOES NOT WARRANT, GUARANTEE OR MAKE ANY REPRESENTATION REGARDING THE ACCURACY, RELIABILITY, CURRENTNESS, USE, OR RESULTS OF USE, OF THE SOFTWARE.

**5. LIMITATION OF REMEDIES AND DAMAGES:** IN NO EVENT SHALL THE COMPANY OR ITS EMPLOYEES, AGENTS, LICENSORS, OR CONTRACTORS BE LIABLE FOR ANY INCIDENTAL, INDIRECT, SPECIAL, OR CONSEQUENTIAL DAMAGES ARISING OUT OF OR IN CONNECTION WITH THIS LICENSE OR THE SOFTWARE, INCLUDING FOR LOSS OF USE, LOSS OF DATA, LOSS OF INCOME OR PROFIT, OR OTHER LOSSES, SUSTAINED AS A RESULT OF INJURY TO ANY PERSON, OR LOSS OF OR DAMAGE TO PROPERTY, OR CLAIMS OF THIRD PARTIES, EVEN IF THE COMPANY OR AN AUTHORIZED REPRESENTATIVE OF THE COMPANY HAS BEEN ADVISED OF THE POSSIBILITY OF SUCH DAMAGES. IN NO EVENT SHALL THE LIABILITY OF THE COMPANY FOR DAMAGES WITH RESPECT TO THE SOFTWARE EXCEED THE AMOUNTS ACTUALLY PAID BY YOU, IF ANY, FOR THE SOFTWARE OR THE ACCOMPANYING TEXTBOOK. BECAUSE SOME JURISDICTIONS DO NOT ALLOW THE LIMITATION OF LIABILITY IN CERTAIN CIRCUMSTANCES, THE ABOVE LIMITATIONS MAY NOT ALWAYS APPLY TO YOU.

**6. GENERAL:** THIS AGREEMENT SHALL BE CONSTRUED IN ACCORDANCE WITH THE LAWS OF THE UNITED STATES OF AMERICA AND THE STATE OF NEW YORK, APPLICABLE TO CONTRACTS MADE IN NEW YORK, EXCLUDING THE STATE'S LAWS AND POLICIES ON CONFLICTS OF LAW, AND SHALL BENEFIT THE COMPANY, ITS AFFILIATES AND ASSIGNEES. THIS AGREEMENT IS THE COMPLETE AND EXCLUSIVE STATEMENT OF THE AGREEMENT BETWEEN YOU AND THE COMPANY AND SUPERSEDES ALL PROPOSALS OR PRIOR AGREEMENTS, ORAL, OR WRITTEN, AND ANY OTHER COMMUNICATIONS BETWEEN YOU AND THE COMPANY OR ANY REPRESENTATIVE OF THE COMPANY RELATING TO THE SUBJECT MATTER OF THIS AGREEMENT. If you are a U.S. Government user, this Software is licensed with "restricted rights" as set forth in subparagraphs (a)-(d) of the Commercial Computer-Restricted Rights clause at FAR 52.227-19 or in subparagraphs (c)(1)(ii) of the Rights in Technical Data and Computer Software clause at DFARS 252.227-7013, and similar clauses, as applicable.

Should you have any questions concerning this agreement or if you wish to contact the Company for any reason, please contact in writing: Customer Service, Pearson Education, Inc., 10 Bank Street, White Plains, NY 10606.

ISBN-13: 978-0-13-240925-4
ISBN-10: 0-13-240925-9
Copyright © 2010 Pearson Education, Inc. All rights reserved.